THE ULTIMATE
CLEVELAND INDIANS
TRIVIA BOOK

A Collection of Amazing Trivia Quizzes and Fun Facts for Die-Hard Indians Fans!

Ray Walker

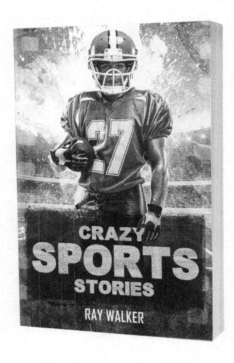

CONTENTS

INTRODUCTION

The Cleveland Indians were established in 1894 and were previously known as the Rustlers, Lake Shores, Blue Birds, Broncos, and Naps. No matter their name, they have consistently proven themselves to be a team that fights hard and is a force to be reckoned with.

They won two World Series championships, in 1920 and 1948. They have won 6 American League pennants, 10 Central Division titles, and 2 wild card berths. They are very often a threat in the American League Central Division, having last won it in 2018. They made their most recent World Series appearance in 2016.

The Indians have retired the uniform numbers of Earl Averill, Lou Boudreau, Larry Doby, Mel Harder, Bob Feller, Frank Robinson, Bob Lemon, and Jim Thome.

The thing about baseball is that it is a lot like life. There are good times and bad times, good days and bad days, but you have to do your absolute best to never give up. The Cleveland Indians have proven that they refuse to give up and that they will do anything they need to do to bring a championship to the state of Ohio.

1

Winning is more than possible when you have a storied past as the Indians do. They have so much captivating history and so many undeniable player legacies to be profoundly proud of.

While calling Progressive Field home, which opened in 1994, they play in one of the most difficult divisions in baseball, the American League Central alongside the Minnesota Twins, Chicago White Sox, Kansas City Royals, Detroit Tigers.

With such a storied team past that goes back generations, you're probably already very knowledgeable as the die-hard Tribe fan that you are. Let's test that knowledge to see if you truly are the world's biggest Indians fan.

CHAPTER 1:

ORIGINS & HISTORY

QUIZ TIME!

1. Which of the following names did the team once use?

    a. Naps

    b. Bluebirds

    c. Broncos

    d. All of the above

2. In what year was the Cleveland franchise established?

    a. 1890

    b. 1894

    c. 1899

    d. 1901

3. The Indians' current home stadium is Progressive Field.

    a. True

    b. False

4. Which division do the Cleveland Indians play in?

    a. American League Central

    b. American League East

c. National League East

d. National League Central

5. The Cleveland Indians have never won a wild card berth.

    a. True

    b. False

6. How many American League pennants has the Indians franchise won (as of the 2020 season)?

    a. 2

    b. 6

    c. 9

    d. 12

7. What is the name of the Indians' mascot?

    a. Chief Wahoo

    b. Pocahontas

    c. Orbit

    d. Slider

8. Who is the winningest manager in Cleveland Indians history (as of the 2020 season)?

    a. Terry Francona

    b. Eric Wedge

    c. Lou Boudreau

    d. Alvin Dark

9. What is the name of Cleveland's Triple-A Team and where is it located?

    a. Indianapolis Indians

    b. Louisville Bats

c. Columbus Clippers

d. Durham Bulls

10. Who was the first manager of the franchise?

a. Nap Lajoie

b. Jimmy McAleer

c. Bill Bradley

d. Roger Peckinpaugh

11. The Cleveland Indians played in the American League East Division from 1969-1993 and moved to the American League Central Division in 1994.

a. True

b. False

12. What is the name of the Indians' spring training home stadium?

a. Hohokam Stadium

b. Sloan Park

c. Goodyear Ballpark

d. Tempe Diablo Stadium

13. How many times has the Cleveland Indians franchise appeared in the MLB playoffs (as of the end of the 2020 season)?

a. 9

b. 11

c. 15

d. 18

14. How many World Series titles have the Indians won (as of the 2020 season)?

    a. 1
    b. 2
    c. 3
    d. 4

15. The Indians never won an AL East Division title during their time in the AL East.

    a. True
    b. False

16. What was the first home stadium of the Cleveland Indians franchise?

    a. Cleveland Stadium
    b. Progressive Field
    c. Indians Ballpark
    d. League Park

17. How many American League pennants have the Cleveland Indians won (as of the end of the 2020 season)?

    a. 3
    b. 6
    c. 7
    d. 9

18. How many American League Central Division titles have the Cleveland Indians won (as of the end of the 2020 season)?

    a. 9
    b. 10

c. 11

d. 12

19. The Cleveland Indians' World Series championship drought since 1948 is currently the longest active drought among the 30 MLB teams.

    a. True

    b. False

20. The Indians franchise NEVER made it to the playoffs when they were the Bluebirds, Broncos, or Naps.

    a. True

    b. False

QUIZ ANSWERS

1. D – All of the above

2. B – 1894

3. A – True

4. A – American League Central

5. B – False (2)

6. B – 6

7. D – Slider

8. C – Lou Boudreau

9. C – Columbus Clippers

10. B – Jimmy McAleer

11. A – True

12. C – Goodyear Ballpark

13. C – 15

14. B – 2

15. A – True

16. D – League Park

17. B – 6

18. B – 10

19. A – True

20. A – True

DID YOU KNOW?

1. The Cleveland franchise has had 46 managers: Jimmy McAleer, Bill Armour, Nap Lajoie, Bill Bradley, Deacon McGuire, George Stovall, Harry Davis, Joe Birmingham, Lee Fohl, Tris Speaker, Jack McCallister, Roger Peckinpaugh, Bibb Falk, Walter Johnson, Steve O' Neill, Ossie Vitt, Lou Boudreau, Al López, Kerby Farrell, Bobby Bragan, Joe Gordon, Jo-Jo White, Jimmy Dykes, Mel Harder, Mel McGaha, Birdie Tebbetts, George Strickland, Joe Adcock, Alvin Dark, Johnny Lipon, Ken Aspromonte, Frank Robinson, Jeff Torborg, Dave Garcia, Mike Ferraro, Pat Corrales, Doc Edwards, John Hart, John McNamara, Mike Hargrove, Charlie Manuel, Joel Skinner, Eric Wedge, Manny Acta, Sandy Alomar Jr., and Terry Francona.

2. The Indians' current manager is Terry Francona. He has previously managed the Boston Red Sox and Philadelphia Phillies. His nickname is "Tito." His father, also named Tito, played in the MLB from 1956 through 1970 with the Indians, Baltimore Orioles, Chicago White Sox, Detroit Tigers, St. Louis Cardinals, Philadelphia Phillies, Atlanta Braves, Oakland A's, and Milwaukee Brewers. Terry Francona played for the Indians, Montreal Expos, Chicago Cubs, Cincinnati Reds, and Milwaukee Brewers from 1981-1990.

3. Lou Boudreau is the Cleveland Indians' all-time winningest manager with a record of 728-649, a .529 winning percentage.

4. Pitcher Bob Feller was the first player to have his number retired by the Cleveland Indians. His number 19 was retired in 1957.

5. The Cleveland Indians have hosted six MLB All-Star Games. The first one was played in 1935 at Cleveland Stadium, the second in 1954 at Cleveland Stadium, the third in 1963 at Cleveland Stadium, the fourth in 1981 at Cleveland Stadium, the fifth in 1997 at Progressive Field, and the latest in 2019 at Progressive Field.

6. Cleveland pitchers have thrown 14 no-hitters. The first occurred in 1901 and the latest was in 1981.

7. Cleveland pitchers have thrown two perfect games, Addie Joss in 1908 and Len Barker in 1981.

8. The Indians' Double-A farm team is the Akron RubberDucks…. yes, the RubberDucks.

9. The Indians' mascot, Slider, is a large, furry fuchsia creature with bushy yellow eyebrows and a furry yellow nose. He made his debut in 1990. His look was inspired by the Phillie Phanatic.

10. Jim Thome is the latest Indian to have his number retired by the team. His number 25 was retired in 2018. That same year, he was inducted into the National Baseball Hall of Fame.

CHAPTER 2:

JERSEYS & NUMBERS

QUIZ TIME!

1. In 2019, for the first time in 70 years, the Indians' uniforms did not feature the Chief Wahoo logo.

    a. True
    b. False

2. For all games, the Indians wear a Navy blue batting helmet with a _____ block "C" on the front.

    a. White
    b. Black
    c. Red
    d. Green

3. Both the home and away uniforms feature the word "Cleveland"; neither says "Indians."

    a. True
    b. False

4. Which of the following numbers has NOT been retired by the Cleveland Indians (as of the end of the 2019 season)?

    a. 3
    b. 5
    c. 14
    d. 15

5. What uniform number does SS Francisco Lindor wear?

    a. 12
    b. 21
    c. 25
    d. 52

6. What uniform number did slugger Jim Thome wear during his time with the Indians?

    a. 6
    b. 25
    c. 59
    d. All of the Above

7. Manny Ramirez's uniform number has been retired by the Cleveland Indians.

    a. True
    b. False

8. Only two Indians players have ever worn the uniform No. 99 in franchise history: James Karinchak and _____.

    a. Adam Cimber
    b. Jason Giambi
    c. Josh Outman
    d. Daniel Robertson

9. Which former Indians manager had his No. 5 retired by the team?

    a. Nap Lajoie
    b. Lou Boudreau
    c. Tris Speaker
    d. Mel Harder

10. Mel Harder's No. 18 was retired by the Cleveland Indians in 1990.

    a. True
    b. False

11. hat are the Cleveland Indians' official team colors?

    a. Red, black, white
    b. B. Navy blue, red, black
    c. C. Navy blue, red, white
    d. D. Navy blue, white, black

12. Who was the first Indian to have his uniform number retired by the team?

    a. Lou Boudreau
    b. Bob Feller
    c. Earl Averill
    d. Mel Harder

13. Jim Thome is the latest to have his uniform number (25) retired by the Indians, in 2018.

    a. True
    b. False

14. What number did Kenny Lofton wear as an Indian?

    a. 7
    b. 12
    c. 28
    d. 46

15. What number did Sam McDowell wear as an Indian?

    a. 34
    b. 48
    c. 55
    d. Both A & B

16. What jersey number did Early Wynn wear as an Indian?

    a. 8
    b. 18
    c. 24
    d. Both B & C

17. What number did Corey Kluber wear with the Indians?

    a. 28
    b. 34
    c. 49
    d. Both A & B

18. What jersey number did Manny Ramirez wear as an Indian?

    a. 6
    b. 12
    c. 24
    d. 99

19. What jersey number did Al Rosen wear as an Indian?

    a. 7

    b. 17

    c. 27

    d. Both A & B

20. The Indians have retired eight uniform numbers (as of the 2020 season).

    a. True

    b. False

QUIZ ANSWERS

1. A - True

2. C – Red

3. B – False (Home uniforms say "Indians," away uniforms say "Cleveland.")

4. D – 15

5. B – 21

6. D – All of the Above

7. B – False

8. D – Daniel Robertson

9. B – Lou Boudreau

10. A – True

11. C – Navy blue, red, white

12. B – Bob Feller

13. A – True

14. A – 7

15. D – Both A & B

16. C – 24

17. D – Both A & B

18. C – 24

19. D – Both A & B

20. A – True

DID YOU KNOW?

1. The Indians have retired eight numbers so far: Earl Averill (No. 3), Lou Boudreau (No. 5), Larry Doby (No. 14), Mel Harder (No. 18), Bob Feller (No. 19), Frank Robinson (No. 20), Bob Lemon (No. 21), and Jim Thome (No. 25).

2. Only three players have ever worn No. 0 for the Indians: Junior Ortiz in 1992-1993, Brandon Barnes (2018), and Delino DeShields (2020).

3. Only two players have ever worn No. 00 for the Indians: Paul Dade in 1977-1979 and Rick White (2004).

4. Jason Giambi is the only Cleveland Indians player ever to wear No. 72. He wore it back in 2014.

5. Adam Cimber is the only Cleveland Indians player ever to wear No. 90. He wore it from 2018 through 2020.

6. Luis Medina is the only Cleveland Indians player ever to wear No. 69. He wore it in 1988.

7. Jackie Robinson's No. 42 has been retired by MLB as a whole. No Indians or MLB player will ever wear No. 42 again. The Yankees' Mariano Rivera was the final player to wear it.

8. Jack Armstrong is the only Cleveland Indians player ever to wear No. 77. He wore it in 1992.

9. During his time with the Indians, Larry Doby wore the uniform numbers 6, 14, and 37.

10. During his career with the Indians, Bob Lemon wore the uniform numbers 6, 21, 38, and 42.

CHAPTER 3:

FAMOUS QUOTES

QUIZ TIME!

1. Which former Indians player once said: "I sign every autograph I can for kids because I remember myself at that age. I think it's ridiculous that some guys won't sign for a kid"?

   a. Manny Ramirez

   b. Nick Swisher

   c. Omar Vizquel

   d. Jim Thome

2. Which former Indians player once said: "Kids are our future and we hope baseball has given them some idea of what it is to live together and how we can get along, whether you be black or white"?

   a. Kenny Lofton

   b. Larry Doby

   c. C.C. Sabathia

   d. Joe Carter

3. Omar Vizquel once said: "The shortstop is a perfectly conditioned athlete. You're running out on relays all the time. You're covering second base. On every pitch, you're moving."

    a. True

    b. False

4. Which Indians manager once said: "As a manager, the more consistent you are, the better off you are. It's easy to be up when things go well. When things don't go well, the players will follow your lead. So you have to be consistent and upbeat, which takes some work sometimes"?

    a. Charlie Manuel

    b. John Hart

    c. Terry Francona

    d. Alvin Dark

5. Which former Indians player once said: "If you put a baseball and other toys in front of a baby, he'll pick up a baseball in preference to the others"?

    a. Tris Speaker

    b. Al Rosen

    c. Earl Averill

    d. Bob Lemon

6. Which former Indians player is quoted as saying: "Every day is a new opportunity. You can build on yesterday's success or put its failures behind and start over again. That's the way life is, with a new game every day, and that's the way baseball is"?

a. Rocky Covalito
b. Addie Joss
c. Ray Chapman
d. Bob Feller

7. Which former Indians pitcher is quoted as saying: "It's no fun throwing fastballs to guys who can't hit them. The real challenge is getting them out on the stuff they can hit"?

a. Corey Kluber
b. Cliff Lee
c. Sam McDowell
d. Bob Lemon

8. Former Indian, Nap Lajoie once said, "A life is not important except in the impact it has on other lives."

a. True
b. False

9. "There'll be a man on the moon before _____ hits a home run." – Alvin Dark

a. Gaylord Perry
b. Mel Harder
c. Bob Lemon
d. Orel Hershiser

10. Which former Indians player is quoted as saying: "I don't believe in curses. I think you make your own destination"?

a. Jason Kipnis
b. Nap Lajoie
c. Manny Ramirez
d. Albert Belle

11. Which former Indians player is quoted as saying: "A lot of people have the ability, but they don't put forth the effort"?

    a. Rick Manning
    b. Roberto Alomar
    c. Dave Winfield
    d. Joe Carter

12. Which former Indians pitcher is quoted as saying, "A pitcher has to look at the hitter as his mortal enemy"?

    a. Addie Joss
    b. Early Wynn
    c. Charles Nagy
    d. Gaylord Perry

13. Which former Indians player is quoted as saying: "I chose baseball because, to me, baseball is the best game of all"?

    a. José Mesa
    b. Dave Winfield
    c. Mike Hargrove
    d. Ray Fosse

14. Which former Indians player is quoted as saying: "I've come to the conclusion that the two most important things in life are good friends and a good bullpen"?

    a. Bob Feller
    b. Al Rosen
    c. Eric Wedge
    d. Bob Lemon

15. Which Indians manager is quoted as saying: "I look at Jimmy [Thome] as a son. I keep telling him he's my son. One reason for that is because he can hit – really hit. If he couldn't, maybe I'd look at him as a nephew or something"?

    a. John McNamara
    b. Charlie Manuel
    c. Mike Hargrove
    d. Eric Wedge

16. Former Indian Bob Feller once said, "Never allow the fear of striking out keep you from playing the game."

    a. True
    b. False

17. Which former Indians player is quoted as saying: "Some plays just come out of me, just on instincts. I'll make a play and wonder, How did I do that?"?

    a. Victor Martinez
    b. Sandy Alomar Jr.
    c. Roberto Alomar
    d. Omar Vizquel

18. Which former Indians player once said: "When you get to the big leagues, you need to take potential and turn it into performance. You want to be the guy who got the most out of his ability, not the guy who never fulfilled his potential"?

    a. Jim Thome
    b. Grady Sizemore

c. Mel Harder

d. Travis Hafner

19. Which former Indians player once said: "I thank the Lord for having the kind of a career that doesn't happen very often to an individual. A lot of times when I was playing, I pinched myself to see if it was really me and if it was really happening. If I had to do it all over again, I wouldn't change anything."

a. Bob Feller

b. Lou Boudreau

c. Jim Thome

d. Manny Ramirez

20. Former Indian Rocky Colavito once said: "If I was traded to the Giants, I'd quit baseball."

a. True

b. False

QUIZ ANSWERS

1. D – Jim Thome

2. B – Larry Doby

3. B – False (Lou Boudreau)

4. C – Terry Francona

5. A – Tris Speaker

6. D – Bob Feller

7. C – Sam McDowell

8. B – False (Jackie Robinson)

9. A – Gaylord Perry

10. C – Manny Ramirez

11. D – Joe Carter

12. B – Early Wynn

13. B – Dave Winfield

14. D – Bob Lemon

15. B – Charlie Manuel

16. B – False (Babe Ruth)

17. C – Roberto Alomar

18. D – Travis Hafner

19. B – Lou Boudreau

20. A – True

DID YOU KNOW?

1. "It's nice to come into a town and be referred to as the manager of the Cleveland Indians, instead of as the first black manager." – Frank Robinson

2. "Cleveland fans are awesome." – LeBron James

3. "Cleveland is my hometown and the Indians have a narrow but rich history." – Fred Willard

4. "The Indians were the only team interested in taking a chance on Albert Belle, and I made the most of it. Hopefully, they got as much from me as I got from them." – Albert Belle

5. "I am going to cherish every single second I am able to play this game. I will not take anything for granted." – Francisco Lindor

6. "I thought I was going to be in Cleveland forever." – Kenny Lofton

7. "As long as we win games while I'm on the mound, I feel good." – C.C. Sabathia

8. "That's what I love about the game. There's always pressure in baseball." – Grady Sizemore

9. "What can I say about Cleveland? Both as a city and an organization, my time in northeast Ohio shaped the person that I am today in so many ways. Dick Jacobs had vision and the teams he built alongside John Hart, Dan

O'Dowd, and Mark Shapiro in the '90s were majestic. The Dolan family is doing an incredible job of continuing that legacy today, and I'm forever grateful that they've been so generous to me and my family over the years.

"I had amazing teammates in those days, wow. The top of that order, Lofton, Vizquel, Baerga, Belle, and my first roomy in the big leagues, Sandy Alomar, and a rock-solid Charles Nagy on the hill, and two veteran leaders to guide us, Eddie Murray and Dave Winfield. To name one of them is to name all of them. They know how special they are to me. Those guys are my brothers. And to my manager, Mike Hargrove, thank you for continuing to write my name in the lineup, even when I struggled. Cleveland is where my career was born." – Jim Thome in his National Baseball Hall of Fame induction speech

10. "BrO-HIO" – Nick Swisher

CHAPTER 4:

CATCHY NICKNAMES

QUIZ TIME!

1. "C.C." is a nickname. What is C.C. Sabathia's full name?

    a. Charles Christopher Sabathia Jr.

    b. Christopher Charles Sabathia Jr.

    c. Carsten Charles Sabathia Jr.

    d. Charles Carsten Sabathia Jr.

2. Corey Kluber goes by the nickname "Klubot."

    a. True

    b. False

3. What nickname does Carlos Santana go by?

    a. Santee

    b. Car-Go

    c. Slamtana

    d. Tana

4. What nickname did Kenny Lofton go by?

    a. Ken-Man

    b. K-Lo

c. Liftoff Lofton

d. Slammin' Kenny

5. Which has NOT been a nickname for the Indians as a team?

   a. The Tribe

   b. The Wahoos

   c. The Windians

   d. The Native Americans

6. "Shoeless Joe" was a nickname. What was Shoeless Joe Jackson's full name?

   a. Joseph Jefferson Jackson

   b. Joseph James Jackson

   c. Joseph Jack Jackson

   d. Joseph Justin Jackson

7. Nap Lajoie went by the nicknames, "Nap," "Larry," and "The Frenchman." His given first name was Napoleon.

   a. True

   b. False

8. Current Indians manager Terry Francona goes by the nickname, _____.

   a. Cona

   b. T-Man

   c. Franc

   d. Tito

9. What was Gaylord Perry's nickname?

   a. The Lord Perry
   b. The Ancient Mariner
   c. The Ancient Indian
   d. Pitchin' Perry

10. What nickname did Bob Feller go by?

   a. Bullet Bob
   b. The Good Feller
   c. BaseBob
   d. Fastball Feller

11. What nickname does Jim Thome go by?

   a. Go Big or Go Thome
   b. Thomer
   c. The Pride of Peoria
   d. Both B and C

12. Albert Belle preferred a cold clubhouse. One day, when a teammate turned up the heat, Belle walked over to the thermostat and smashed it with a bat. His nickname from there on out was "Mr. Freeze."

   a. True
   b. False

13. What nickname does Omar Vizquel go by?

   a. Big O
   b. Little O
   c. Big V
   d. Little V

14. What is Michael Brantley's nickname?

    a. Big Mike
    b. Dr. Fast
    c. Dr. Cool
    d. Dr. Smooth

15. Tris Speaker went by the nicknames "Tris" and "the Gray Eagle." His real first name was Tristram.

    a. True
    b. False

16. Francisco Lindor has the nickname _____.

    a. Lindie
    b. Big Franny
    c. Paquito
    d. Cisco

17. During Player's Weekend, Shane Bieber chose the nickname "Not Justin."

    a. True
    b. False

18. What nickname does Bartolo Colon go by?

    a. Big Sexy
    b. Little Sexy
    c. Big Guy
    d. Tolo-Colo

19. What nickname did Mike Hargrove go by?

    a. The Human Rain Delay
    b. Grover

c. Big Mike

d. Both A and B

20. Mel Harder had the nickname "Chief."

a. True

b. False

QUIZ ANSWERS

1. C – Carsten Charles Sabathia Jr.

2. A – True

3. C – Slamtana

4. B – K-Lo

5. D – The Native Americans

6. A – Joseph Jefferson Jackson

7. A – True

8. D – Tito

9. B – The Ancient Mariner

10. A – Bullet Bob

11. D – Both B and C

12. A – True

13. B – Little O

14. D – Dr. Smooth

15. A – True

16. C – Paquito

17. A – True

18. A – Big Sexy

19. D – Both A and B

20. A – True

DID YOU KNOW?

1. José Mesa was given the nickname "José Table" because that is the translation of his name from Spanish to English.

2. Early in his career, Asdrubal Cabrera was given the nickname "Baby Omar" because of his similarity to Omar Vizquel.

3. "Coco" is a nickname. Coco Crisp's given name is Covelli Loyce Crisp. He got the nickname from his sister, who teased him that he looked like one of the characters on the Cocoa Krispies box. He officially changed his name to Coco on March 5, 2013.

4. Former Indian Early Wynn went by the simple nickname "Gus."

5. Former Indian Adrian "Addie" Joss went by the nicknames, "Human Hairpin" and "Human Slat."

6. Manny Ramirez has many nicknames, including Manny Being Manny, Mannywood, and Man-Ram. His given first name is Manuel.

7. Lou Boudreau went by the nickname, "Good Kid."

8. Former Indian Earl Averill went by the nickname "the Earl of Snohomish." He was born in Snohomish, Washington.

9. Former Indian Al Rosen, who was Jewish, had the nickname "the Hebrew Hammer."

10. Former Indian Sam McDowell went by the nickname "Sudden Sam" because of his fastball.

CHAPTER 5:

THE PRIDE OF PEORIA

QUIZ TIME!

1. What is Jim Thome's full name?

    a. Howard James Thome

    b. James Howard Thome

    c. James Michael Thome

    d. Michael James Thome

2. During his MLB career, Jim Thome played for the Indians, Philadelphia Phillies, Chicago White Sox, Los Angeles Dodgers, Minnesota Twins, and Baltimore Orioles.

    a. True

    b. False

3. Where was Jim Thome born?

    a. Lima, Ohio

    b. Cleveland, Ohio

    c. Chicago, Illinois

    d. Peoria, Illinois

4. When was Jim Thome born?

    a. April 27, 1969
    b. April 27, 1970
    c. August 27, 1970
    d. August 27, 1969

5. Jim Thome only won one Silver Slugger Award in his entire career.

    a. True
    b. False

6. How many MLB All-Star Games was Jim Thome named to in his career?

    a. 0
    b. 2
    c. 5
    d. 7

7. Where did Jim Thome go to college?

    a. Western Illinois University
    b. Illinois Central College
    c. University of Chicago
    d. University of Illinois at Chicago

8. Jim Thome was drafted by the Cleveland Indians in 1989.

    a. True
    b. False

9. How many home runs did Jim Thome hit in his career?

    a. 412
    b. 512

c. 612

d. 712

10. How many hits did Jim Thome collect during his career?

a. 2,238

b. 2,328

c. 2,438

d. 2,538

11. How many years did Jim Thome play in the MLB?

a. 19

b. 20

c. 21

d. 22

12. A fan poll in *The Plain Dealer* in 2003 named Jim Thome the most popular athlete in Cleveland sports history.

a. True

b. False

13. What year was Jim Thome inducted into the National Baseball Hall of Fame?

a. 2016

b. 2017

c. 2018

d. 2019

14. Jim Thome was inducted into the National Baseball Hall of Fame in his first year of eligibility with 89.8% of the vote.

a. True

b. False

15. How many times was Jim Thome walked in his career?

    a. 1,647
    b. 1,747
    c. 1,847
    d. 1,949

16. Jim Thome began his career with the Indians and ended his career with the _____.

    a. Philadelphia Phillies
    b. Minnesota Twins
    c. Chicago White Sox
    d. Baltimore Orioles

17. Jim Thome received a Roberto Clemente Award in 2002.

    a. True
    b. False

18. How many World Series championships did Jim Thome win?

    a. 0
    b. 1
    c. 2
    d. 3

19. The Cleveland Indians have retired Jim Thome's No. ___.

    a. 6
    b. 25
    c. 34
    d. 59

20. Besides being a great baseball player, Jim Thome is known for his positive attitude and philanthropy.

    a. True

    b. False

QUIZ ANSWERS

1. B – James Howard Thome

2. A – True

3. D – Peoria, Illinois

4. C – August 27, 1970

5. A – True

6. C – 5

7. B – Illinois Central College

8. A – True

9. C – 612

10. B – 2,328

11. D – 22

12. A – True

13. C– 2018

14. A – True

15. B – 1,747

16. D – Baltimore Orioles

17. True

18. A – 0

19. B – 25

20. A – True

DID YOU KNOW?

1. Upon retiring, Jim Thome accepted an executive position with the Chicago White Sox organization as special assistant to the general manager. He also serves as an analyst on MLB Network.

2. Thome and his wife Andrea have two children: Lila and Landon.

3. While he was a player, Thome established funds to put his 10 nieces and nephews through college.

4. Jim Thome takes part in an annual event to raise money for the Children's Hospital of Illinois, a tradition his mother started years ago.

5. Twins pitcher Joe Nathan said of Thome, "He's the world's nicest man."

6. Every year before spring training, Thome visited his former high school.

7. Thome was known for wearing high socks and for his very unique batting stance.

8. Jim Thome was the first Cleveland player to be inducted into the National Baseball Hall of Fame as an Indian without Chief Wahoo on his plaque.

9. On August 2, 2014, Thome signed a one-day contract with Cleveland to retire officially from baseball as a member of the Indians.

10. Thome is a member of the Indians' Hall of Fame and the Philadelphia Phillies' Wall of Fame. Only the Indians have retired his jersey number, though.

CHAPTER 6:

STATISTICALLY SPEAKING

QUIZ TIME!

1. Jim Thome holds the Cleveland Indians franchise record for the most home runs. How many did he hit?

   a. 327

   b. 337

   c. 347

   d. 357

2. Pitcher Bob Feller has the most wins in Cleveland Indians franchise history with 266.

   a. True

   b. False

3. Which pitcher holds the Cleveland Indians record for shutouts with 45?

   a. Bob Feller

   b. Bob Lemon

   c. Addie Joss

   d. Stan Coveleski

4. Which Cleveland Indians hitter holds the single-season record for strikeouts with 194?

    a. Jim Thome

    b. Cory Snyder

    c. Grady Sizemore

    d. Mike Napoli

5. Which pitcher has the most strikeouts in franchise history with a whopping 2,581?

    a. Sam McDowell

    b. Bob Feller

    c. Corey Kluber

    d. C.C Sabathia

6. _____ has the most stolen bases in Cleveland Indians franchise history with 452.

    a. Omar Vizquel

    b. Terry Turner

    c. Harry Bay

    d. Kenny Lofton

7. Cody Allen holds the record for most saves in Cleveland Indians history with 149.

    a. True

    b. False

8. _____ holds the Cleveland Indians record for being intentionally walked with 87.

    a. Travis Hafner

    b. Andre Thornton

c. Jim Thome

d. Victor Martinez

9. Which player holds the franchise record for home runs in a single season with 52?

a. Albert Belle

b. Manny Ramirez

c. Jim Thome

d. Al Rosen

10. Which batter holds the single-season franchise record for hits with 233?

a. Shoeless Joe Jackson

b. Nap Lajoie

c. Earl Averill

d. George Burns

11. Who holds the single-season Cleveland Indians record for double plays grounded into with 28?

a. Victor Martinez

b. Julio Franco

c. Jhonny Peralta

d. Buddy Bell

12. Omar Vizquel holds the record for the most sacrifice flies in franchise history with 62.

a. True

b. False

13. Sam McDowell threw the wildest pitches in Cleveland Indians franchise history with how many?

a. 65

b. 83

c. 114

d. 123

14. Shoeless Joe Jackson holds the Cleveland Indians single-season record for most triples. How many did he hit in his record 1912 season?

a. 12

b. 16

c. 20

d. 26

15. Which hitter has the most walks in Cleveland Indians franchise history with 1,008?

a. Carlos Santana

b. Jim Thome

c. Tris Speaker

d. Larry Doby

16. Which Cleveland Indians hitter holds the all-time franchise record for best career batting average at .375?

a. Shoeless Joe Jackson

b. Tris Speaker

c. Roberto Alomar

d. Lew Fonseca

17. Kenny Lofton holds the Cleveland Indians record for most runs scored with 1,154.

a. True

b. False

18. Earl Averill has the most plate appearances all-time in Cleveland Indians franchise history with how many?

    a. 6,412
    b. 6,512
    c. 6,612
    d. 6,712

19. Which pitcher holds the Cleveland Indians franchise record for most saves in a single season with 46?

    a. Joe Borowski
    b. Bob Wickman
    c. José Mesa
    d. Chris Perez

20. Mel Harder holds the Cleveland Indians franchise record for most losses with 186.

    a. True
    b. False

QUIZ ANSWERS

1. B – 337

2. A – True

3. C – Addie Joss

4. D – Mike Napoli (2016)

5. B – Bob Feller

6. D – Kenny Lofton

7. A – True

8. C – Jim Thome

9. C – Jim Thome (2002)

10. A – Shoeless Joe Jackson

11. B – Julio Franco (1986)

12. A – True

13. C – 114

14. D – 26

15. B – Jim Thome

16. A – Shoeless Joe Jackson

17. B – False, Earl Averill

18. D – 6,712

19. C – José Mesa (1995)

20. A – True

DID YOU KNOW?

1. Bob Feller threw the most innings in Cleveland Indians franchise history with 3,827.0. Coming in second is Mel Harder, who threw 3,426.1 innings.

2. Shoeless Joe Jackson had the best and second-best single-season batting average in Cleveland Indians franchise history at .408 in 1911 and .395 in 1912.

3. Roberto Alomar holds the Cleveland Indians franchise record for stolen base percentage with an 86.89% success rate. Kenny Lofton holds the franchise record for stolen bases with 452 and Charlie Jamieson holds the franchise record for the most times caught stealing with 110.

4. Earl Averill has the most extra-base hits in Cleveland Indians franchise history with 724. Second on the list is Tris Speaker with 667.

5. Jim Thome holds the Cleveland Indians franchise record for at-bats per home run at 14.0. This means that, during his time with Cleveland, Thome hit a home run about every 14 at-bats.

6. Danny Salazar holds the Cleveland Indians franchise record for strikeouts per 9 innings pitched at 10.471. That means that, during his time with Cleveland, Salazar recorded between 10 and 11 strikeouts in every 9 innings that he pitched.

7. Ryan Garko holds the single-season Cleveland Indians record for the most hit by pitches with 20 in 2007. Otto Hess holds the single-season Cleveland Indians record for most batters hit with 24 in 1906.

8. Tris Speaker holds the Cleveland Indians franchise record for doubles with 486. Second on the list is Nap Lajoie with 424.

9. Jim Bagby holds the Cleveland Indians single-season record for wins with 31 in 1920.

10. Pete Dowling holds the Cleveland Indians single-season record for losses with 22 in 1901.

CHAPTER 7:

THE TRADE MARKET

QUIZ TIME!

1. On June 27, 2002, the Cleveland Indians traded
   _____ and Tim Drew to the Montreal Expos
   in exchange for Cliff Lee, Brandon Phillips, Grady
   Sizemore, and Lee Stevens.

   a. Bartolo Colon
   b. Coco Crisp
   c. Victor Martinez
   d. C.C. Sabathia

2. On December 6, 1989, the Cleveland Indians traded Joe
   Carter to the San Diego Padres in exchange for
   _____, Carlos Baerga, and Chris James.

   a. Roberto Alomar
   b. Sandy Alomar Jr.
   c. Dave Clark
   d. Bud Black

3. The Cleveland Indians have NEVER made a trade with the Arizona Diamondbacks.

   a. True
   b. False

4. On July 7, 2008, the Indians traded _____ to the Milwaukee Brewers in exchange for Michael Brantley, Rob Bryson, Zach Jackson, and Matt LaPorta.

   a. John Axford
   b. David Bell
   c. C.C. Sabathia
   d. Tony Fernandez

5. The Cleveland Indians have made only seven trades with the Colorado Rockies (as of the end of the 2019 season).

   a. True
   b. False

6. What year did the Cleveland Indians receive Tris Speaker from the Boston Red Sox?

   a. 1914
   b. 1915
   c. 1916
   d. 1918

7. On July 29, 2009, the Cleveland Indians traded _____ and Ben Francisco to the Philadelphia Phillies in exchange for Carlos Carrasco, Jason Donald, Jason Knapp, and Lou Marson.

   a. Michael Bourn
   b. Asdrubal Cabrera

c. Jay Bruce

d. Cliff Lee

8. Which team traded Corey Kluber to the Cleveland Indians at the trade deadline in 2010?

   a. Texas Rangers

   b. San Diego Padres

   c. St. Louis Cardinals

   d. Los Angeles Dodgers

9. On March 24, 1973, the Cleveland Indians traded _____ and Jack Heidemann to the Oakland A's in exchange for Dave Duncan and George Hendrick.

   a. Ray Fosse

   b. Harold Baines

   c. Dennis Eckersley

   d. Alfredo Griffin

10. The Cleveland Indians have made only four trades with the Miami Marlins (as of the end of the 2020 season).

    a. True

    b. False

11. At the trade deadline in 2016, the Cleveland Indians sent J.P. Feyereisen, Clint Frazier, Ben Heller, and Justus Sheffield to the New York Yankees in exchange for

_____.

   a. Joba Chamberlain

   b. Melky Cabrera

   c. Andrew Miller

   d. Edwin Encarnacion

12. On August 17, 1960, the Cleveland Indians traded Rocky Colavito to the Detroit Tigers in exchange for Harvey Kuenn.

    a. True
    b. False

13. How many trades have the Cleveland Indians made with the Tampa Bay Rays (as of the end of the 2019 season)?

    a. 7
    b. 11
    c. 14
    d. 21

14. As of the end of the 2019 season, the Cleveland Indians have not made a trade with the Kansas City Royals since 2004.

    a. True
    b. False

15. On October 25, 1955, the Cleveland Indians traded Larry Doby to the _____ in exchange for Jim Busby and Chico Carrasquel.

    a. Chicago Cubs
    b. Detroit Tigers
    c. Chicago White Sox
    d. Baltimore Orioles

16. From what team did the Cleveland Indians acquire Trevor Bauer on December 11, 2012?

    a. Cincinnati Reds
    b. Arizona Diamondbacks

    c. New York Yankees

    d. Los Angeles Dodgers

17. To what team did the Cleveland Indians trade Shin-Soo Choo on December 11, 2012?

    a. Texas Rangers

    b. Seattle Mariners

    c. Los Angeles Angels of Anaheim

    d. Cincinnati Reds

18. On December 20, 1993, the Cleveland Indians traded Felix Fermin, Reggie Jefferson, and cash to the Seattle Mariners in exchange for _____.

    a. Bud Black

    b. Pat Borders

    c. José Mesa

    d. Omar Vizquel

19. On March 25, 1997, the Cleveland Indians traded _____ and Alan Embree to the Atlanta Braves in exchange for David Justice and Marquis Grissom.

    a. Bartolo Colon

    b. Derek Lilliquist

    c. Kenny Lofton

    d. Terry Mulholland

20. The Cleveland Indians never traded Jim Thome.

    a. True

    b. False

QUIZ ANSWERS

1. A – Bartolo Colon

2. B – Sandy Alomar Jr.

3. B – False (Five trades as of the end of the 2019 season.)

4. C – C.C. Sabathia

5. A – True

6. C – 1916

7. D – Cliff Lee

8. B – San Diego Padres

9. A – Ray Fosse

10. A – True

11. C – Andrew Miller

12. A – True

13. C – 14

14. A – True

15. C – Chicago White Sox

16. B – Arizona Diamondbacks

17. D – Cincinnati Reds

18. D – Omar Vizquel

19. C – Kenny Lofton

20. A – True

DID YOU KNOW?

1. At the trade deadline in 2009, the Cleveland Indians sent Victor Martinez to the Boston Red Sox in exchange for Nick Hagadone, Justin Masterson, and Bryan Price.

2. On June 6, 1983, the Cleveland Indians Rick Manning and Rick Waits to the Milwaukee Brewers for Ernie Camacho, Jamie Easterly, and Gorman Thomas.

3. On August 31, 2016, the Oakland A's traded Coco Crisp back to the Cleveland Indians in exchange for Colt Hynes.

4. On July 30, 2011, the Cleveland Indians traded Orlando Cabrera to the San Francisco Giants in exchange for Thomas Neal.

5. On July 29, 1996, the Cleveland Indians traded Carlos Baerga and Alvaro Espinoza to the New York Mets in exchange for Jeff Kent and José Vizcaino.

6. On July 28, 2010, the Cleveland Indians traded Jhonny Peralta and cash to the Detroit Tigers in exchange for Giovanni Soto.

7. On December 15, 2019, the Cleveland Indians traded Corey Kluber to the Texas Rangers in exchange for Delino DeShields and Emmanuel Clase.

8. On August 31, 2018, the Cleveland Indians acquired Josh Donaldson from the Toronto Blue Jays in exchange for a player to be named later (Julian Merryweather).

9. At the trade deadline in 2014, the Cleveland Indians traded Asdrubal Cabrera and cash to the Washington Nationals in exchange for Zach Walters.

10. At the trade deadline in 2019, the Cleveland Indians acquired Yasiel Puig from the Cincinnati Reds.

CHAPTER 8:

DRAFT DAY

QUIZ TIME!

1. With the _____ overall pick in the 1st round of the 1991 MLB draft, the Cleveland Indians selected Manny Ramirez.

    a. 1st

    b. 6th

    c. 13th

    d. 21st

2. In the 13th round of the 1989 MLB draft, the Cleveland Indians selected _____.

    a. Albert Belle

    b. Jim Thome

    c. Kenny Lofton

    d. José Mesa

3. With the 8th overall pick in the 1st round of the 2011 MLB draft, the Cleveland Indians selected _____.

    a. Francisco Lindor

    b. José Ramirez

c. Michael Bourn

d. Lonnie Chisenhall

4. With the 7th overall pick in 1st round of the 1965 MLB draft, the Cleveland Indians selected _____.

a. José Cardenal

b. Sam McDowell

c. Lou Piniella

d. Ray Fosse

5. With the 16th overall pick in the 1st round of the 2002 MLB draft, the _____ selected Nick Swisher.

a. New York Yankees

b. Chicago White Sox

c. Oakland A's

d. Cleveland Indians

6. With the 17th overall pick in the 1st round of the 1988 MLB draft, the Cleveland Indians selected _____.

a. Albert Belle

b. Charles Nagy

c. Doug Jones

d. Carlos Baerga

7. With the 5th overall pick in the 1st round of the 2010 MLB draft, the Cleveland Indians selected Drew Pomeranz.

a. True

b. False

8. With the 20th overall pick in the 1st round of the 1998 MLB draft, the Cleveland Indians selected _____.

a. Omar Vizquel

b. Ellis Burks

c. Milton Bradley

d. C.C. Sabathia

9. Kenny Lofton was drafted in the 17th round of the 1988 MLB draft by the _____.

a. Pittsburgh Pirates

b. Houston Astros

c. Los Angeles Dodgers

d. Atlanta Braves

10. The Cleveland Indians drafted Coco Crisp in the 7th round of the 1999 MLB draft.

a. True

b. False

11. Grady Sizemore was drafted in the 3rd round of the 2000 MLB draft by the _____.

a. Philadelphia Phillies

b. Boston Red Sox

c. Montreal Expos

d. Tampa Bay Devil Rays

12. Travis Hafner was drafted in the 31st round of the 1996 MLB draft by the Texas Rangers.

a. True

b. False

13. With the 2nd overall pick in the 1st round of the 1972 MLB draft, the Cleveland Indians selected _____.

a. Alfredo Griffin

b. Rick Manning

c. Alan Ashby

d. George Hendrick

14. In the _____ round of the 2009 MLB draft, the Cleveland Indians selected Jason Kipnis.

a. 2nd

b. 4th

c. 8th

d. 12th

15. Corey Kluber was drafted in the 4th round of the 2007 MLB draft by the _____.

a. Texas Rangers

b. San Diego Padres

c. Minnesota Twins

d. Los Angeles Dodgers

16. With the 3rd overall pick in the 1st round of the 2011 MLB draft, the _____ selected Trevor Bauer.

a. Cincinnati Reds

b. Los Angeles Angels of Anaheim

c. New York Yankees

d. Arizona Diamondbacks

17. With the 29th overall pick in the 1st round of the 2008 MLB draft, the Cleveland Indians selected _____.

a. Michael Brantley

b. José Ramirez

c. Lonnie Chisenhall

d. Yan Gomes

18. Mark Rzepczynski was drafted in the 5th round of the 2007 MLB draft by the _____.

a. Washington Nationals

b. Seattle Mariners

c. Toronto Blue Jays

d. St. Louis Cardinals

19. With the ____ overall pick in the 1st round of the 1984 MLB draft, the Cleveland Indians selected Cory Snyder.

a. 2nd

b. 4th

c. 6th

d. 8th

20. Dennis Eckersley was drafted by the Cleveland Indians in the 3rd round of the 1972 MLB draft.

a. True

b. False

QUIZ ANSWERS

1. C – 13th

2. B – Jim Thome

3. A – Francisco Lindor

4. D – Ray Fosse

5. C – Oakland A's

6. B – Charles Nagy

7. A – True

8. D – C.C. Sabathia

9. B – Houston Astros

10. B – False (St. Louis Cardinals)

11. C – Montreal Expos

12. A – True

13. B – Rick Manning

14. A – 2nd

15. B – San Diego Padres

16. D – Arizona Diamondbacks

17. C – Lonnie Chisenhall

18. C – Toronto Blue Jays

19. B – 4th

20. A – True

DID YOU KNOW?

1. Cliff Lee was drafted in 1997 by the Florida Marlins but did not sign. He was drafted again in 1998 by the Baltimore Orioles but once again did not sign. Finally, he was drafted in the 4th round of the 2000 MLB draft by the Montreal Expos where did ultimately sign.

2. The Cleveland Indians drafted Alan Ashby in the 3rd round of the 1969 MLB draft out of high school.

3. The Milwaukee Brewers drafted Michael Brantley in the 7th round of the 2005 MLB draft out of high school.

4. Michael Bourn was drafted by the Houston Astros in the 19th round of the 2000 draft out of high school but did not sign. He was then drafted by the Philadelphia Phillies in the 4th round of the 2003 MLB draft out of the University of Houston.

5. With the 11th overall pick in the 1st round of the 1983 MLB draft, the Cleveland Indians selected Dave Clark out of Jackson State University.

6. Milton Bradley was drafted by the Montreal Expos in the 2nd round of the 1996 MLB draft out of high school.

7. Brandon Phillips was drafted by the Montreal Expos in the 2nd round of the 1999 MLB draft out of high school.

8. The Houston Astros drafted Delino DeShields Jr. in the 1st round of the 2010 MLB draft, 8th overall. His father played in the MLB for 13 seasons.

9. Terry Mulholland was drafted by the San Francisco Giants in the 1st round, 24th overall, in the 1984 MLB draft.

10. David Justice was drafted by the Atlanta Braves in the 4th round of the 1985 MLB draft.

CHAPTER 9:

ODDS & ENDS

QUIZ TIME!

1. Which BRAVO reality show has Johnny Damon appeared on twice?

    a. Vanderpump Rules
    b. Below Deck
    c. The Real Housewives of Beverly Hills
    d. Southern Charm

2. Kenny Lofton co-wrote the song "What If," which is on American Idol winner Ruben Studdard's 2006 album, *Soulful.*

    a. True
    b. False

3. Terry Francona has been best friends with Indians _____coach, Brad Mills since their college playing days. They coached together with the Red Sox and Phillies as well.

    a. Pitching
    b. First

c. Hitting

d. Bench

4. The character of Sam Malone, played by Ted Danson in the television show _____, was based on the life of Sam McDowell.

   a. Seinfeld

   b. Frasier

   c. Cheers

   d. Everybody Loves Raymond

5. After retiring from baseball in 1956, Al Rosen became a

   _____.

   a. Real estate agent

   b. Stockbroker

   c. Plumber

   d. Hot tub salesman

6. Former Indian Jeff Kent appeared on which TV reality show?

   a. Big Brother

   b. Survivor

   c. The Amazing Race

   d. American Ninja Warrior

7. Jason Giambi's brother Jeremy also played in the major leagues.

   a. True

   b. False

8. Nick Swisher is married to which actress?

   a. Jessica Biel
   b. Emma Roberts
   c. Lea Michele
   d. Joanna Garcia

9. In April 2006, Malley's Chocolates of Cleveland unveiled the "Pronk Bar," a milk chocolate candy bar made in honor of _____.

   a. Jhonny Peralta
   b. Travis Hafner
   c. Grady Sizemore
   d. Ryan Garko

10. _____ founded a cattle ranch called "Victoria's Ranch" once he retired from baseball.

   a. Bob Lemon
   b. Jhonny Peralta
   c. Victor Martinez
   d. Cliff Lee

11. Which former Indians manager joined *Baseball Tonight* on ESPN as a studio analyst for the 2014-2015 seasons alongside Dallas Braden and Ozzie Guillen?

   a. John Hart
   b. Eric Wedge
   c. Sandy Alomar Jr.
   d. Charlie Manuel

12. Brandon Phillips' sister Porsha plays in the WNBA for the San Antonio Silver Stars.

   a. True
   b. False

13. In 2003, former Indians player/manager Frank Robinson guest-starred in an episode of _____ alongside MLB legends Ernie Banks and Johnny Bench.

   a. King of Queens
   b. Seinfeld
   c. Everybody Loves Raymond
   d. Yes, Dear

14. Milton Bradley's great-great-grandfather created the Milton Bradley game company.

   a. True
   b. False

15. In a 1994 episode of _____, Dave Winfield appeared with other MLB players as themselves during the MLB strike.

   a. Friends
   b. The Fresh Prince of Bel-Air
   c. Married with Children
   d. Sister, Sister

16. Ellis Burks is a cousin of fellow former MLB outfielder Roosevelt Brown.

   a. True
   b. False

17. From what college did Bud Black a bachelor's degree in management?

    a. Oregon State University
    b. Colorado State University
    c. Long Beach State University
    d. San Diego State University

18. Dennis Eckersley is a part-time color commentator for which MLB team?

    a. Oakland A's
    b. Boston Red Sox
    c. Cleveland Indians
    d. Chicago Cubs

19. Manny Ramirez once tried to sell his _____ on eBay.

    a. Flat-screen TV
    b. Old iPhone
    c. Barbeque grill
    d. Lawnmower

20. Shane Bieber is the brother of singer Justin Bieber.

    a. True
    b. False

QUIZ ANSWERS

1. B – Below Deck

2. A – True

3. D – Bench

4. C – Cheers

5. B – Stockbroker

6. B – Survivor

7. A – True

8. D – Joanna Garcia

9. B – Travis Hafner

10. C – Victor Martinez

11. B – Eric Wedge

12. A – True

13. D – Yes, Dear

14. B – False

15. C – Married with Children

16. A – True

17. D – San Diego State University

18. B – Boston Red Sox

19. C – Barbeque Grill

20. B – False

DID YOU KNOW?

1. Larry Doby became the second black manager in the MLB when he was named manager of the Chicago White Sox in 1978. He was also a director of the New Jersey Nets of the NBA.

2. In 1997, Kenny Lofton made a guest appearance on *The Wayans Bros.* and in 2004 he made a guest appearance on the show *George Lopez.*

3. During the COVID-19 pandemic, former Indian Shin-Soo Choo donated $1,000 to 190 of the Texas Rangers' minor leaguers who were unable to play during the shutdown. When he was in the minors, he used to skip meals to be able to buy diapers for his newborn.

4. C.C. Sabathia was born in Vallejo, California, and currently resides in Fairfield, California, close to where he was born and raised.

5. In July 2017, Coco Crisp became the head coach of the Shadow Hills High School baseball team. In 2019, he joined the Oakland Athletics Radio Network as a color analyst part-time.

6. Sandy Alomar Jr. is the son of former MLB player Sandy Alomar and brother of fellow former Indian, Roberto Alomar.

7. When Bartolo Colon was 42 years old, he became the oldest MLB player to hit his first career home run. At 45

years old, he was the oldest active MLB player and the last active MLB player who had played for the Montreal Expos. He also holds the record for most wins by a pitcher born in Latin America.

8. Michael Brantley is the son of former MLB player and hitting coach Mickey Brantley.

9. In 2011, Nick Swisher released a children's album called "Believe." It featured fellow MLB players Barry Zito and Bernie Williams. It peaked at No. 3 on iTunes' Top Children's Albums.

10. Former Indians players Sean Casey, Bill Ripken, Jim Thome, and Mark DeRosa and former Indians manager/ general manager John Hart are all currently on-air personalities on MLB Network.

CHAPTER 10:

OUTFIELDERS

QUIZ TIME!

1. Manny Ramirez played eight seasons with the Cleveland Indians. Which of the teams below did he NOT play for during his 19-season career?

   a. Boston Red Sox
   b. Los Angeles Dodgers
   c. Chicago White Sox
   d. Los Angeles Angels of Anaheim

2. Grady Sizemore was never named to an MLB All-Star Game in his 10-year MLB career.

   a. True
   b. False

3. What year was Larry Doby inducted into the National Baseball Hall of Fame?

   a. 1996
   b. 1997
   c. 1998
   d. 1999

4. Joe Carter did NOT win a World Series championship in his 16-year MLB career.

   a. True
   b. False

5. How many MLB All-Star Games was Earl Averill named to in his 13-year MLB career?

   a. 2
   b. 4
   c. 6
   d. 8

6. So far in his MLB career, Michael Brantley has played for the Cleveland Indians and the _____ (as of the 2020 season).

   a. Houston Astros
   b. Chicago Cubs
   c. Boston Red Sox
   d. Los Angeles Dodgers

7. Shin-Soo Choo played seven seasons with the Cleveland Indians.

   a. True
   b. False

8. Rajai Davis played for eight different MLB teams during his 14-year MLB career. He played for the Indians, Toronto Blue Jays, San Francisco Giants, Pittsburgh Pirates, Detroit Tigers, New York Mets, Boston Red Sox and the _____.

a. New York Yankees

b. Baltimore Orioles

c. Kansas City Royals

d. Oakland Athletics

9. What year was Dave Winfield inducted into the National Baseball Hall of Fame?

   a. 2000

   b. 2001

   c. 2002

   d. 2003

10. How many Gold Glove Awards did Michael Bourn win during his 11-year MLB career?

    a. 1

    b. 2

    c. 3

    d. 4

11. How many seasons did Coco Crisp play for the Cleveland Indians?

    a. 3

    b. 4

    c. 5

    d. 6

12. Current Cleveland Indians manager Terry Francona played for the Indians for one season.

    a. True

    b. False

13. How many MLB All-Star Games was Nick Swisher named to during his 12-year MLB career?

    a. 1
    b. 2
    c. 4
    d. 5

14. Former Indians outfielder Dave Roberts is currently the manager of which MLB team?

    a. San Francisco Giants
    b. Boston Red Sox
    c. San Diego Padres
    d. Los Angeles Dodgers

15. During his 13-year MLB career, Rick Manning played for the Indians and the _____.

    a. Milwaukee Brewers
    b. St. Louis Cardinals
    c. Montreal Expos
    d. Atlanta Braves

16. What year was Ralph Kiner inducted into the National Baseball Hall of Fame?

    a. 1974
    b. 1975
    c. 1976
    d. 1978

17. How many Silver Slugger Awards did Ellis Burks win during his 18-year MLB career?

a. 0

b. 1

c. 2

d. 3

18. How many Gold Glove Awards did Grady Sizemore win during his 10-year MLB career?

    a. 0

    b. 2

    c. 4

    d. 5

19. How many home runs did Manny Ramirez hit during his eight seasons with the Cleveland Indians?

    a. 201

    b. 236

    c. 274

    d. 299

20. Former Indians outfielder Mark DeRosa is currently an analyst on MLB Network.

    a. True

    b. False

QUIZ ANSWERS

1. D – Los Angeles Angels of Anaheim

2. B – False (He was a 3x All-Star.)

3. C – 1998

4. B – False (He was a 2x World Series champion.)

5. C – 6

6. A – Houston Astros

7. A – True

8. D – Oakland Athletics

9. B – 2001

10. B – 2

11. C – 5

12. A – True

13. A – 1

14. D – Los Angeles Dodgers

15. A – Milwaukee Brewers

16. B – 1975

17. C – 2

18. B – 2

19. B – 236

20. A – True

DID YOU KNOW?

1. Larry Doby played 1,235 games for the Cleveland Indians, the most of any team he played for during his 13-year MLB career. He also played for the Chicago White Sox and the Detroit Tigers. He is a member of the National Baseball Hall of Fame, a World Series champion, and 7x MLB All-Star.

2. Manny Ramirez played 967 games for the Cleveland Indians, the second most of any team he played for during his 19-year MLB career. He also played for the Boston Red Sox, Los Angeles Dodgers, Chicago White Sox, and Tampa Bay Rays. He is a 2x World Series champion, World Series MVP, 9x Silver Slugger Award winner, 12x MLB All-Star, and batting title champion.

3. Grady Sizemore played 892 games for the Cleveland Indians, the most of any team he played for in his 10-year MLB career. He also played for the Philadelphia Phillies, Tampa Bay Rays, and Boston Red Sox. He is a Silver Slugger Award winner, 3x MLB All-Star, and 2x Gold Glove Award winner.

4. Joe Carter played 839 games for the Cleveland Indians, the second most of any team he played for during his 16-year MLB career. He also played for the Toronto Blue Jays, San Diego Padres, San Francisco Giants, Chicago Cubs, and Baltimore Orioles. He is a 5x MLB All-Star, 2x Silver Slugger Award winner, and 2x World Series champion.

5. Earl Averill played 1,510 games for the Cleveland Indians, the most of any team he played for in his 13-year MLB career. He also played for the Detroit Tigers and Boston Braves. He is a member of the National Baseball Hall of Fame and a 6x MLB All-Star.

6. Dave Winfield played only 46 games for the Cleveland Indians, the least of any team he played for during his 22-year MLB career. He also played for the New York Yankees, San Diego Padres, Minnesota Twins, California Angels, and Toronto Blue Jays. He is a member of the National Baseball Hall of Fame, a 12x MLB All-Star, World Series champion, 7x Gold Glove Award winner, and 6x Silver Slugger Award winner.

7. Michael Bourn played 331 games in the three seasons he spent with the Cleveland Indians. In his 11-year MLB career, he also played for the Houston Astros, Atlanta Braves, Philadelphia Phillies, Baltimore Orioles, and Arizona Diamondbacks. He is a 2x MLB All-Star, 2x Gold Glove Award winner, and a Wilson Overall Defensive Player of the Year Award winner.

8. Coco Crisp played 435 games in the five seasons he spent with the Indians, the second most of any team he played for. In his 15-year MLB career, he also played for the Oakland A's, Boston Red Sox, and Kansas City Royals. He began and ended his career with the Indians. He is also a World Series champion.

9. Ohio native Nick Swisher played 272 games in the three seasons he spent with the Cleveland Indians. During his

12-year MLB career, he also played for the Oakland A's, New York Yankees, Chicago White Sox, and Atlanta Braves. He is an MLB All-Star and World Series champion.

10. Ellis Burks played 317 games in the three seasons he spent with the Cleveland Indians. In his 18-year MLB career, he also played for the Colorado Rockies, Boston Red Sox, San Francisco Giants, and Chicago White Sox. He is a Gold Glove Award winner, 2x MLB All-Star, and 2x Silver Slugger Award winner.

CHAPTER 11:

INFIELDERS

QUIZ TIME!

1. What year was Lou Boudreau inducted into the National Baseball Hall of Fame?

    a. 1968

    b. 1969

    c. 1970

    d. 1973

2. Jim Thome did NOT win a Gold Glove Award in his 22-year MLB career.

    a. True

    b. False

3. How many MLB All-Star Games was Al Rosen named to during his 10-year MLB career?

    a. 3

    b. 4

    c. 5

    d. 6

4. How many Gold Glove Awards did Omar Vizquel win in his 24-year MLB career?

   a. 8
   b. 9
   c. 10
   d. 11

5. Carlos Santana has played for two teams so far in his MLB career, the Indians and the _____ (as of the 2020 season).

   a. Texas Rangers
   b. Chicago White Sox
   c. Miami Marlins
   d. Philadelphia Phillies

6. How many MLB All-Star Games was Jason Kipnis named to during the nine years he spent with the Indians?

   a. 0
   b. 2
   c. 3
   d. 5

7. Asdrubal Cabrera won the 2019 World Series with the Washington Nationals.

   a. True
   b. False

8. How many seasons did Travis Hafner play for the Cleveland Indians?

   a. 7
   b. 8

c. 10

d. 12

9. During his 15-year MLB career, Jhonny Peralta played for the Indians, St. Louis Cardinals and the _____.

    a. Kansas City Royals

    b. Detroit Tigers

    c. Milwaukee Brewers

    d. Pittsburgh Pirates

10. How many Gold Glove Awards did Brandon Phillips win during his 17-year MLB career?

    a. 0

    b. 2

    c. 4

    d. 5

11. How many MLB All-Star Games was Lou Boudreau named to in his 15-year MLB career?

    a. 2

    b. 4

    c. 6

    d. 8

12. Al Rosen was named the 1953 American League MVP.

    a. True

    b. False

13. What year did Francisco Lindor win an American League Platinum Glove Award?

a. 2016

b. 2017

c. 2018

d. 2019

14. Which two seasons did José Ramirez win back-to-back Silver Slugger Awards?

    a. 2014-2015

    b. 2015-2016

    c. 2017-2018

    d. 2018-2019

15. Which current famous MLB star is Yonder Alonso the brother-in-law of?

    a. Mike Trout

    b. Manny Machado

    c. Aaron Judge

    d. Nolan Arenado

16. Jason Giambi ended his 20-year MLB career with the Indians in 2014.

    a. True

    b. False

17. Over the course of his MLB career, Mike Napoli played for the Indians, Los Angeles Angels of Anaheim, Texas Rangers, and _____.

    a. Colorado Rockies

    b. Tampa Bay Rays

    c. Boston Red Sox

    d. New York Yankees

18. How many Gold Glove Awards did Orlando Cabrera win during his 15-year MLB career?

    a. 1
    b. 2
    c. 3
    d. 4

19. What year was Nap Lajoie inducted into the National Baseball Hall of Fame?

    a. 1931
    b. 1933
    c. 1935
    d. 1937

20. Josh Barfield, son of Toronto Blue Jays great Jesse Barfield, played second base for the Indians from 2007-2009.

    a. True
    b. False

QUIZ ANSWERS

1. C – 1970

2. A – True

3. B – 4

4. D – 11

5. D – Philadelphia Phillies

6. B – 2

7. A – True

8. C – 10

9. B – Detroit Tigers

10. C – 4

11. D – 8

12. A – True

13. A – 2016

14. C – 2017-2018

15. B – Manny Machado

16. A – True

17. C – Boston Red Sox

18. B – 2

19. D – 1937

20. A – True

DID YOU KNOW?

1. Lou Boudreau played for the Cleveland Indians for 13 seasons. During his 15-year MLB career, he also played for the Boston Red Sox. He is a member of the National Baseball Hall of Fame, an MVP, 8x MLB All-Star, World Series champion, batting title champion, and Major League Player of the Year. He played 1,560 games with the Indians. He went on to manage the Indians, Red Sox, Kansas City Athletics, and Chicago Cubs.

2. Nap Lajoie played for the Cleveland Indians for 13 seasons. During his 21-year MLB career, he also played for the Philadelphia Phillies and Philadelphia Athletics. He is a member of the National Baseball Hall of Fame, a Triple Crown winner, and a 3x batting title champion. He played 1,614 games with the Indians.

3. Jim Thome played for the Cleveland Indians for 13 seasons. In his 22-year MLB career, he also played for the Philadelphia Phillies, Chicago White Sox, Minnesota Twins, Los Angeles Dodgers, and Baltimore Orioles. He is a member of the National Baseball Hall of Fame, a 5x MLB All-Star, and Silver Slugger Award winner. He played 1,399 games with the Indians.

4. Al Rosen played his entire 10-year MLB career with the Cleveland Indians. He is a World Series champion, a 4x MLB All-Star, MVP, and Major League Player of the Year. He played 1,044 games with the Indians.

5. Omar Vizquel played for the Cleveland Indians for 11 seasons. During his 24-year MLB career, he also played for the Seattle Mariners, San Francisco Giants, Chicago White Sox, Texas Rangers, and Toronto Blue Jays. He is an 11x Gold Glove Award winner and 3x MLB All-Star. He played 1,478 games with the Indians.

6. Jason Kipnis played for the Cleveland Indians for nine seasons. So far in his career, he has also played for the Chicago Cubs. As of the 2020 season, he is a 2x MLB All-Star. He played 1,121 games with the Indians.

7. Francisco Lindor has played his entire career with the Cleveland Indians (so far, at least). At this point in his career, he is a 2x Gold Glove Award winner, Platinum Glove Award winner, 4x MLB All-Star, and 2x Silver Slugger Award winner.

8. José Ramirez has played his entire career with the Cleveland Indians (so far, at least). At this point in his career, he is a 2x MLB All-Star and 2x Silver Slugger Award winner.

9. Brandon Phillips played for the Cleveland Indians for four seasons. During his 17-year MLB career, he also played for the Cincinnati Reds, Atlanta Braves, Boston Red Sox, and Los Angeles Angels of Anaheim. He is a 4x Gold Glove Award winner, 3x MLB All-Star, and Silver Slugger Award winner. He played 135 games with the Indians.

10. Joe Sewell played for the Cleveland Indians for 11 seasons. In his 14-year MLB career, he also played for the New

York Yankees. He is a member of the National Baseball Hall of Fame and a 2x World Series champion. He played 1,513 games with the Indians.

CHAPTER 12:

PITCHERS AND CATCHERS

QUIZ TIME!

1. Former Indians catcher Ray Fosse is currently a TV broadcaster for the _____.

    a. Seattle Mariners
    b. Cincinnati Reds
    c. Oakland A's
    d. Kansas City Royals

2. C.C. Sabathia won a Cy Young Award as a member of the Indians in 2007.

    a. True
    b. False

3. What year was Bob Feller named to the National Baseball Hall of Fame?

    a. 1960
    b. 1962
    c. 1965
    d. 1966

4. So far in his MLB career, Corey Kluber has pitched for the Indians and the _____ (as of the 2020 season).

    a. San Diego Padres
    b. Minnesota Twins
    c. Chicago Cubs
    d. Texas Rangers

5. What year was Sandy Alomar Jr. named the American League Rookie of the Year?

    a. 1989
    b. 1990
    c. 1993
    d. 1995

6. How many Cy Young Awards did Gaylord Perry win during his 22-year MLB career?

    a. 2
    b. 4
    c. 6
    d. 9

7. Mel Harder played his entire 20-year MLB career with the Cleveland Indians.

    a. True
    b. False

8. What year was Bob Lemon inducted into the National Baseball Hall of Fame?

    a. 1972
    b. 1974

c. 1976

d. 1978

9. How many different MLB teams did Bartolo Colon play for in his 21-year MLB career?

    a. 7

    b. 9

    c. 11

    d. 15

10. How many Silver Slugger Awards did Victor Martinez win during his 16-year MLB career?

    a. 0

    b. 2

    c. 3

    d. 5

11. In his 23-year MLB career, Cliff Lee pitched for the Indians, Texas Rangers, Seattle Mariners, and _____.

    a. Colorado Rockies

    b. Pittsburgh Pirates

    c. Los Angeles Angels of Anaheim

    d. Philadelphia Phillies

12. Bob Lemon missed the 1943, 1944, and 1945 MLB seasons due to military service.

    a. True

    b. False

13. What year was Addie Joss inducted into the National Baseball Hall of Fame?

    a. 1972

    b. 1974

    c. 1976

    d. 1978

14. How many Cy Young Awards did Dennis Eckersley win during his 24-year MLB career?

    a. 1

    b. 3

    c. 5

    d. 9

15. Charles Nagy pitched for two teams in his 14-year MLB career: the Indians and the _____.

    a. New York Mets

    b. Arizona Diamondbacks

    c. Detroit Tigers

    d. San Diego Padres

16. Yan Gomes won a Silver Slugger Award as a member of the Indians in 2014.

    a. True

    b. False

17. How many saves did José Mesa record during his seven seasons with the Cleveland Indians?

    a. 84

    b. 94

c. 104

d. 114

18. How many MLB All-Star Games was Doug Jones named to during his 16-year MLB career?

    a. 2

    b. 4

    c. 5

    d. 7

19. Former Indians pitcher Bud Black is currently the manager of which MLB team?

    a. San Diego Padres

    b. Colorado Rockies

    c. New York Mets

    d. Miami Marlins

20. Early Wynn was a 9x MLB All-Star.

    a. True

    b. False

QUIZ ANSWERS

1. C – Oakland A's

2. A – True

3. B – 1962

4. D – Texas Rangers

5. B – 1990

6. A – 2

7. A – True

8. C – 1976

9. C – 11

10. B – 2

11. D – Philadelphia Phillies

12. A – True

13. D – 1978

14. A – 1

15. D – San Diego Padres

16. A – True

17. C – 104

18. C – 5

19. B – Colorado Rockies

20. A – True

DID YOU KNOW?

1. Pitcher C.C. Sabathia played for the Cleveland Indians for eight seasons. During his 19-year MLB career, he also pitched for the New York Yankees and Milwaukee Brewers. He is a Cy Young Award winner, a 6x MLB All-Star, ALCS MVP, and World Series champion. His record with the Indians was 106-71.

2. Catcher Ray Fosse played for the Cleveland Indians for eight seasons. In his 12-year MLB career, he also played for the Oakland A's, Seattle Mariners, and Milwaukee Brewers. He is a 2x MLB All-Star, 2x Gold Glove Award winner, and 2x World Series champion. He is currently a TV and radio broadcaster for the A's.

3. Pitcher Bob Feller played for the Cleveland Indians for his entire 18-year MLB career. He missed three MLB seasons due to military service. He is a member of the National Baseball Hall of Fame, a Triple Crown winner, World Series champion, Major League Player of the Year, ERA title winner, and 8x MLB All-Star.

4. Pitcher Gaylord Perry played for the Cleveland Indians for four seasons. During his 22-year MLB career, he also played for the San Francisco Giants, Texas Rangers, San Diego Padres, Seattle Mariners, Kansas City Royals, Atlanta Braves, and New York Yankees. He is a member of the National Baseball Hall of Fame, a 2x Cy Young Award

winner, and 5x MLB All-Star. His record with the Indians was 70-57.

5. Pitcher Mel Harder played for the Cleveland Indians for his entire 20-year MLB career. He was a 4x MLB All-Star. His career record was 223-186.

6. Pitcher Bob Lemon played for the Cleveland Indians for his entire 13-year MLB career. He is a member of the National Baseball Hall of Fame, a 7x MLB All-Star, and World Series champion. His career record was 207-128. He missed three MLB seasons due to military service.

7. Catcher Sandy Alomar Jr. played for the Cleveland Indians for 11 seasons, the most of any team he played for in his 20-year MLB career, he also played for the Chicago White Sox, San Diego Padres, New York Mets, Colorado Rockies, Los Angeles Dodgers, and Texas Rangers. He is a Rookie of the Year Award winner, 6x MLB All-Star, All-Star Game MVP, and Gold Glove Award winner.

8. Pitcher Dennis Eckersley played for the Cleveland Indians for three seasons. In his 24-year MLB career, he also played for the Oakland A's, Boston Red Sox, Chicago Cubs, and St. Louis Cardinals. He is a member of the National Baseball Hall of Fame, a Cy Young Award winner, a 56x MLB All-Star, World Series champion, ALCS MVP, MVP, and 2x Rolaids Reliever of the Year Award winner. His record with the Indians was 40-32.

9. Pitcher Early Wynn played for the Cleveland Indians for 10 seasons. During his 23-year MLB career, he also pitched

for the Washington Senators and Chicago White Sox. He is a member of the National Baseball Hall of Fame, a 9x MLB All-Star, Cy Young Award winner, ERA Title winner, and Major League Player of the Year. His record with the Indians was 164-102. He missed one MLB season due to military service.

10. There have been 14 no-hitters and 2 perfect games in Cleveland franchise history. Indians pitchers who have thrown no-hitters/perfect games are Pete Dowling, Bob Rhoads, Addie Joss (PG) (2), Ray Caldwell, Wes Ferrell, Bob Feller (3), Don Black, Bob Lemon, Sonny Siebert, Dick Bosman, Dennis Eckersley, and Len Barker (PG).

CHAPTER 13:

WORLD SERIES

QUIZ TIME!

1. How many World Series have the Cleveland Indians won?

    a. 0

    b. 1

    c. 2

    d. 3

2. How many AL pennants have the Cleveland Indians won (as of the end of the 2020 season)?

    a. 2

    b. 4

    c. 6

    d. 8

3. Which team did the Cleveland Indians face in the 1920 World Series?

    a. Brooklyn Robins

    b. Philadelphia Athletics

    c. New York Yankees

    d. St. Louis Browns

4. Which team did the Cleveland Indians face in the 1948 World Series?

    a. Chicago Cubs
    b. Pittsburgh Pirates
    c. St. Louis Braves
    d. Boston Braves

5. Which team did the Cleveland Indians face in the 1954 World Series?

    a. Brooklyn Dodgers
    b. New York Giants
    c. Milwaukee Braves
    d. Philadelphia Phillies

6. Which team did the Cleveland Indians face in the 1995 World Series?

    a. Cincinnati Reds
    b. Los Angeles Dodgers
    c. Atlanta Braves
    d. New York Mets

7. The Cleveland Indians faced the Florida Marlins in the 1997 World Series.

    a. True
    b. False

8. Which team did the Cleveland Indians face in the 2016 World Series?

    a. Los Angeles Dodgers
    b. Chicago Cubs

c. Washington Nationals

d. St. Louis Cardinals

9. Who was the Cleveland Indians manager during their 1995 and 1997 World Series runs?

   a. John Hart

   b. John McNamara

   c. Mike Hargrove

   d. Charlie Manuel

10. Who was the Cleveland Indians manager during their 2016 World Series run?

   a. Mike Hargrove

   b. Charlie Manuel

   c. Eric Wedge

   d. Terry Francona

11. How many games did the 1920 World Series go?

   a. 4

   b. 5

   c. 6

   d. 7

12. The 1948 World Series went six games.

   a. True

   b. False

13. How many games did the 1954 World Series go?

   a. 4

   b. 5

c. 6

d. 7

14. How many games did the 1995 World Series go?

    a. 4

    b. 5

    c. 6

    d. 7

15. How many games did the 1997 World Series go?

    a. 4

    b. 5

    c. 6

    d. 7

16. The 2016 World Series went seven games.

    a. True

    b. False

17. The New York Giants beat the Indians in the 1954 World Series. The Giants franchise did not win another World Series until _____.

    a. 2002

    b. 2010

    c. 2012

    d. 2014

18. In 2016, the Indians lost the World Series championship to the Chicago Cubs, who had not won a World Series title in _____ years.

a. 88
b. 98
c. 108
d. 118

19. Former Indians and Cubs player _____ threw out the ceremonial first pitch before Game 1 of the 2016 World Series at Progressive Field.

    a. Kenny Lofton
    b. Joe Carter
    c. Dennis Eckersley
    d. Milton Bradley

20. The Cleveland Indians have never won a wild card berth.

    a. True
    b. False

QUIZ ANSWERS

1. C – 2

2. C – 6

3. A – Brooklyn Robins

4. D – Boston Braves

5. B – New York Giants

6. C – Atlanta Braves

7. A – True

8. B – Chicago Cubs

9. C – Mike Hargrove

10. D – Terry Francona

11. D – 7

12. A – True

13. A – 4

14. C – 6

15. D – 7

16. A – True

17. B – 2010

18. C – 108

19. A – Kenny Lofton

20. B – False (2013 and 2020)

DID YOU KNOW?

1. The 1920 World Series was the last World Series until 1980 to feature two franchises who had NOT previously won a championship.

2. The 1948 World Series was the only World Series from 1947 through 1958 to not feature a team from New York. It was also the last World Series not won by a New York team until 1957.

3. The 2017 World Series was the first in which home-field advantage was determined by which team had the best regular-season record.

4. The Florida Marlins' World Series win over the Indians in 1997 made the Marlins the first wild card team in MLB history to win the championship.

5. The 2016 World Series featured the two teams with the longest World Series championship droughts, a combined 176 years without a title.

6. The 1995 World Series took place from October 21 through October 28. The 1997 World Series took place from October 18 through October 26. The 2016 World Series took place from October 25 through November 2.

7. Game 1 of the 1954 World Series was played at the Polo Grounds in New York. Jim Barbieri threw out the first pitch. Game 4 of the 1954 World Series was played at

Cleveland Stadium in Cleveland. Jeff Chandler sang the National Anthem.

8. Game 1 of the 1995 World Series was played at the Atlanta-Fulton County Stadium in Atlanta. Cal Ripken Jr. threw out the first pitch and Darius Rucker sang the National Anthem. Game 6 of the 1995 World Series was played at Atlanta-Fulton County Stadium. Jimmy Carter, the 39th U.S. President, threw out the first pitch and The Rembrandts sang the National Anthem.

9. Game 1 of the 1997 World Series was played at Pro Player Park in Miami. Shomari Dailey threw out the first pitch and Hanson sang the National Anthem. Game 7 of the 1997 World Series was played at Pro Player Park. Toni Giamatti threw out the first pitch and Mary Chapin Carpenter sang the National Anthem.

10. Game 1 of the 2016 World Series was played at Progressive Field in Cleveland. Kenny Lofton threw out the first pitch and Rachel Platten sang the National Anthem. Game 7 of the 2016 World Series was played at Progressive Field. Jim Thome threw out the first pitch and the Cleveland Orchestra performed the National Anthem.

CHAPTER 14:

HEATED RIVALRIES

QUIZ TIME!

1. Which team does NOT play in the American League Central with the Indians?

    a. Chicago White Sox

    b. Milwaukee Brewers

    c. Detroit Tigers

    d. Kansas City Royals

2. The Cleveland Indians were in the American League East Division from 1969-1993.

    a. True

    b. False

3. Which team below was formerly a member of the American League East?

    a. Texas Rangers

    b. Houston Astros

    c. Toronto Blue Jays

    d. Milwaukee Brewers

4. What division did the Astros play in from 1969-1993?

    a. American League Central
    b. National League East
    c. National League West
    d. National League Central

5. What is a series with Ohio rival the Cincinnati Reds called?

    a. Buckeye Series
    b. Battle of Ohio
    c. Detroit-Superior Bridge Series
    d. Both A & B

6. What is the name of the trophy given to the winner of a series between the Indians and Cincinnati Reds?

    a. Cuyahoga Cup
    b. Cleveland Cup
    c. Ohio Cup
    d. Cincinnati Cup

7. The Cleveland Indians have the most American League East championships of any team in the division.

    a. True
    b. False

8. The Indians have won two World Series championships. How many have the Detroit Tigers won?

    a. 0
    b. 2
    c. 4
    d. 5

9. The Indians have won two World Series championships. How many have the Chicago White Sox won?

   a. 0
   b. 1
   c. 2
   d. 3

10. The Indians have won two World Series championships. How many have the Cincinnati Reds won?

    a. 1
    b. 3
    c. 5
    d. 7

11. Which player has NOT played for both the Indians and the Detroit Tigers?

    a. Earl Averill
    b. Joba Chamberlain
    c. Larry Doby
    d. Ray Fosse

12. The Cleveland Indians and Cincinnati Reds have never faced each other in the World Series.

    a. True
    b. False

13. Which player has NOT played for both the Indians and the Chicago White Sox?

    a. Roberto Alomar
    b. Johnny Damon

c. Jim Thome

d. Manny Ramirez

14. Which player has NOT played for both the Indians and the Cincinnati Reds?

    a. Brandon Phillips

    b. Trevor Bauer

    c. Victor Martinez

    d. Shin-Soo Choo

15. How many American League East Division championships did the Cleveland Indians win when they were in that division from 1969 through 1993?

    a. 0

    b. 1

    c. 3

    d. 5

16. As of the end of the 2020 season, the last time the Indians won the AL East Division was 2018.

    a. True

    b. False

17. Which team did the Cleveland Indians face in the 2020 wild card series?

    a. Oakland A's

    b. New York Yankees

    c. Chicago White Sox

    d. Tampa Bay Rays

18. Which player has NOT played for both the Indians and the Kansas City Royals?

    a. Coco Crisp
    b. Gaylord Perry
    c. Lou Piniella
    d. Michael Bourn

19. Which player has NOT played for both the Indians and the Minnesota Twins?

    a. Josh Donaldson
    b. C.C. Sabathia
    c. Tris Speaker
    d. Early Wynn

20. The Cleveland Indians have the longest World Series championship drought not only in the American League Central but in MLB as a whole.

    a. True
    b. False

QUIZ ANSWERS

1. B – Milwaukee Brewers

2. A – True

3. D – Milwaukee Brewers

4. C – National League West

5. D – Both A & B

6. C – Ohio Cup

7. A – True (10)

8. C – 4

9. D – 3

10. C – 5

11. D – Ray Fosse

12. A – True

13. B – Johnny Damon

14. C – Victor Martinez

15. A – 0

16. A – True

17. B – New York Yankees

18. D – Michael Bourn

19. B – C.C. Sabathia

20. A – True

DID YOU KNOW?

1. The Cleveland Indians have the most American League East championships with 10, as of the end of the 2020 season. The Minnesota Twins have 8, the Detroit Tigers have 4, the Chicago White Sox have 3, the Kansas City Royals have 1. When the Milwaukee Brewers were in the American League East, they never won a division championship.

2. The American League Central is one of two divisions in MLB all of whose members have won a World Series championship. Each team has actually won at least twice.

3. As of the end of the 2019 season, the Indians are ahead of the Reds with a head-to-head record of 60-53.

4. The Indians and Reds are about 250 miles apart via I-71. The Indians currently hold the Ohio Cup.

5. In 1910, the Reds and Naps played a seven-game series called the "Championship of Ohio" after the regular season ended. The Reds ended up winning the series 4-3 games, with the home team winning every game. Another Championship of Ohio took place in 1911.

6. 1997 was the first season that the Indians and Reds faced each other in the regular season, thanks to the implementation of interleague play.

7. Since 2010, the Indians and Reds have shared Goodyear Park in Arizona as their spring training site.

8. Yonder Alonso, Trevor Bauer, Buddy Bell, Aaron Boone, Jay Bruce, Marlon Byrd, Orlando Cabrera, Shin-Soo Choo, Edwin Encarnacion, Tony Fernandez, Terry Francona, Kevin Mitchell, Brandon Phillips, Yasiel Puig, Frank Robinson, Adam Rosales, and Drew Stubbs have all played for both the Indians and the Cincinnati Reds.

9. Earl Averill, Mike Aviles, George Burns, Sean Casey, Joba Chamberlain, Rocky Colavito, Johnny Damon, Rajai Davis, Larry Doby, Red Donahue, Adam Everett, John Farrell, Cecil Fielder, Tito Francona, Juan Gonzalez, Austin Jackson, Leonys Martin, Victor Martinez, Zach McAllister, José Mesa, Andrew Miller, and Jhonny Peralta have all played for both the Indians and the Detroit Tigers.

10. Roberto Alomar, Sandy Alomar, Yonder Alonso, Earl Averill, Harold Baines, Alan Bannister, Albert Belle, Bobby Bonds, Pat Borders, Ellis Burks, Melky Cabrera, Orlando Cabrera, Steve Carlton, Tyler Clippard, Rocky Colavito, Bartolo Colon, Ross Detwiler, Larry Doby, Alan Embree, Edwin Encarnacion, Tito Francona, Austin Jackson, Shoeless Joe Jackson, Tommy John, Brent Lillibridge, Kenny Lofton, Blue Moon Odom, Tony Pena, Manny Ramirez, Nick Swisher, Jim Thome, Juan Uribe, Omar Vizquel, and Early Wynn have all played for both the Indians and the Chicago White Sox.

CHAPTER 15:

THE AWARDS SECTION

QUIZ TIME!

1. Which Cleveland Indians pitcher won an American League Cy Young Award in 2007?

    a. Roy Oswalt

    b. Jake Westbrook

    c. C.C. Sabathia

    d. Cliff Lee

2. No Cleveland Indians player has ever won the Wilson Defensive Player of the Year Award.

    a. True

    b. False

3. Which Cleveland Indians player won a Silver Slugger Award in 2008?

    a. Grady Sizemore

    b. Asdrubal Cabrera

    c. Shin-Soo Choo

    d. Both A & B

4. Which Cleveland Indians player most recently won the Rookie of the Year Award (as of the end of the 2020 season)?

    a. Herb Score
    b. Chris Chambliss
    c. Joe Charboneau
    d. Sandy Alomar Jr.

5. Who is the only pitcher in Cleveland Indians history to win the Reliever of the Year Award (as of the end of the 2020 season)?

    a. Chris Perez
    b. José Mesa
    c. Kerry Wood
    d. Rafael Betancourt

6. Which former Cleveland Indians player was named the 2008 Sporting News Comeback Player of the Year?

    a. Jhonny Peralta
    b. Grady Sizemore
    c. Cliff Lee
    d. Travis Hafner

7. No Cleveland Indians manager has ever won a Manager of the Year Award.

    a. True
    b. False

8. Which Indians player was named the DHL Hometown Hero, voted by MLB fans as the most outstanding player in franchise history?

a. Jim Thome

b. Nap Lajoie

c. Omar Vizquel

d. Bob Feller

9. Who was the first Cleveland Indians player to win an American League Gold Glove Award?

   a. Minnie Miñoso

   b. Vic Power

   c. Ray Fosse

   d. Sandy Alomar Jr.

10. How many Silver Slugger Awards did Jim Thome win with the Cleveland Indians?

    a. 0

    b. 1

    c. 4

    d. 5

11. How many Silver Slugger Awards did Manny Ramirez win with the Cleveland Indians?

    a. 0

    b. 1

    c. 2

    d. 3

12. Cleveland Indians pitcher Shane Bieber won a Triple Crown in the 2020 season.

    a. True

    b. False

13. Lou Boudreau was named the _____ MLB MVP.

  a. 1946
  b. 1947
  c. 1948
  d. 1949

14. Former Indians pitcher Corey Kluber won the A: Cy Young Award in both 2014 and _____.

  a. 2016
  b. 2017
  c. 2018
  d. 2019

15. What year were the Cleveland Indians named the Baseball America Organization of the Year?

  a. 1992
  b. 1995
  c. 1997
  d. 2016

16. No Cleveland Indians player has ever won the Home Run Derby.

  a. True
  b. False

17. Which former Cleveland Indians pitcher won a Cy Young Award in 1972?

  a. Dick Tidrow
  b. Steve Dunning
  c. Denny Riddleberger
  d. Gaylord Perry

18. How many Gold Glove Awards did Omar Vizquel win with the Cleveland Indians?

    a. 2

    b. 4

    c. 6

    d. 8

19. How many Gold Glove Awards did Kenny Lofton win with the Cleveland Indians?

    a. 2

    b. 4

    c. 6

    d. 8

20. Corey Kluber was named the 2014 American League MVP.

    a. True

    b. False

QUIZ ANSWERS

1. C – C.C. Sabathia

2. B – False (Roberto Perez in 2019)

3. A – Grady Sizemore

4. D – Sandy Alomar Jr. (1990)

5. B – José Mesa (1995)

6. C – Cliff Lee

7. B – False (Eric Wedge in 2007 and Terry Francona in 2013 and 2016)

8. D – Bob Feller

9. A – Minnie Miñoso (1959)

10. B – 1 (1996)

11. D – 3 (1995, 1999, 2000)

12. True

13. C - 1948

14. B - 2017

15. A – 1992

16. A – True

17. D – Gaylord Perry

18. D – 8 (1994-2001 consecutively)

19. B – 4 (1993-1996 consecutively)

20. B – False (Mike Trout, Los Angeles Angels of Anaheim)

DID YOU KNOW?

1. The Cleveland Indians have had four pitchers win the Cy Young Award: Gaylord Perry (1972), C.C. Sabathia (2007), Cliff Lee (2008), and Corey Kluber (2014 and 2017).

2. The Cleveland Indians have had 18 players win Silver Slugger Awards: Andre Thornton (1984), Julio Franco (1988), Carlos Baerga (1992, 1993), Albert Belle (1993-1996), Manny Ramirez (1995, 1999, 2000), Jim Thome (1996), David Justice (1997), Matt Williams (1997), Roberto Alomar (1999, 2000), Juan Gonzalez (2001), Victor Martinez (2004), Grady Sizemore (2008), Asdrubal Cabrera (2011), Michael Brantley (2014), Yan Gomes (2014), Francisco Lindor (2017, 2018), José Ramirez (2017, 2018), and Carlos Santana (2019).

3. The Cleveland Indians have had four players who won Rookie of the Year Awards: Herb Score (1955), Chris Chambliss (1971), Joe Charboneau (1980), and Sandy Alomar Jr. (1990).

4. The Cleveland Indians have had 15 different players win Gold Glove Awards: Minnie Miñoso (1959), Vic Power (958-1961), Jim Piersall (1961), Vic Davalillo (1964), Ray Fosse (1970, 1971), Rick Manning (1976), Sandy Alomar Jr. (1990), Kenny Lofton (1993-1996), Omar Vizquel (1994-2001), Matt Williams (1997), Roberto Alomar (1999-2001), Travis Fryman (2000), Grady Sizemore (2007, 2008), Francisco Lindor (2016, 2019) and Roberto Pérez (2019).

5. Only three Cleveland Indians players have ever won MVP Awards: George Burns (1926), Lou Boudreau (1948), and Al Rosen (1953).

6. There have been only two Triple Crown winners in franchise history: Bob Feller (1940) and Shane Bieber (2020).

7. Cleveland Indians players who have been named *Sporting News'* Player of the Year are Johnny Allen (1937), Bob Feller (1940), Lou Boudreau (1948), Al Rosen (1953), and Albert Belle (1995).

8. The World Series MVP Award did not exist the two times the Indians won the World Series (1920 and 1948), so no Cleveland Indians player has ever been named World Series MVP.

9. Cleveland Indians ALCS MVPs include Orel Hershiser (1995), Marquis Grissom (1997), and Andrew Miller (2016).

10. Cleveland Indians Ford C. Frick Award recipients include Mel Allen and Jimmy Dudley.

CHAPTER 16:

THE 216

QUIZ TIME!

1. Which superhero was created in Cleveland?

   a. The Green Arrow

   b. Batman

   c. Superman

   d. The Flash

2. Cleveland was the first city to be lighted by electricity.

   a. True

   b. False

3. Cleveland is home to the _____ Hall of Fame.

   a. National Radio

   b. Pro Football

   c. National Baseball

   d. Rock & Roll

4. Which game show host was born in Cleveland?

   a. Alex Trebek

   b. Drew Carey

c. Pat Sajak

d. Wayne Brady

5. What is the name of the 52-story skyscraper in Public Square in Downtown Cleveland?

    a. Willis Tower

    b. Vista Tower

    c. Devon Tower

    d. Terminal Tower

6. Which snack was first mass-produced in Cleveland?

    a. Pretzels

    b. Granola bars

    c. Potato chips

    d. Both A & C

7. American Greetings Corporation's headquarters are located in Cleveland.

    a. True

    b. False

8. Which popular candy was invented in Cleveland?

    a. M&Ms

    b. Sweet Tarts

    c. Life Savers

    d. Jolly Ranchers

9. What is the name of Cleveland's NFL team?

    a. Cleveland Eagles

    b. Cleveland Browns

c. Cleveland Cowboys

d. Cleveland 49ers

10. What is the name of Cleveland's NBA team?

a. Cleveland Kings

b. Cleveland Nets

c. Cleveland Warriors

d. Cleveland Cavaliers

11. The Browns play in what home stadium?

a. Paul Brown Stadium

b. FirstEnergy Stadium

c. Heinz Field

d. Bank of America Stadium

12. Cleveland used to have an NHL team called the Cleveland Barons.

a. True

b. False

13. What is the name of the Cavaliers' arena?

a. Rocket Mortgage FieldHouse

b. Chase Center

c. Golden 1 Center

d. Little Caesars Arena

14. Which modern sports ball was invented in Cleveland?

a. The baseball

b. The football

c. The soccer ball

d. The golf ball

15. Which celebrity is from Cleveland?

   a. Halle Berry
   b. Bob Hope
   c. Arsenio Hall
   d. All of the Above

16. Parts of *The Avengers*, *A Christmas Story*, and *Men in Black* were filmed in Cleveland.

   a. True
   b. False

17. What is the name of the performing arts center in Downtown Cleveland (it's the second largest in the United States after the Lincoln Center in New York)?

   a. Kimmel Center
   b. Guthrie Center
   c. Playhouse Square
   d. Kennedy Center

18. What is Cleveland Hopkins International Airport's code?

   a. CHA
   b. CLE
   c. CHE
   d. CLH

19. Cleveland is located on the southern shore of Lake _____.

   a. Superior
   b. Tahoe
   c. Powell
   d. Erie

20. Cleveland has never hosted a Super Bowl.

    a. True
    b. False

QUIZ ANSWERS

1. C – Superman

2. A – True

3. D – Rock & Roll

4. B – Drew Carey

5. D – Terminal Tower

6. C – Potato Chips

7. A – True

8. C – Life Savers

9. B – Cleveland Browns

10. D – Cleveland Cavaliers

11. B – FirstEnergy Stadium

12. A – True

13. A – Rocket Mortgage FieldHouse

14. D – The Golf Ball

15. D – All of the Above

16. A – True

17. C – Playhouse Square

18. B – CLE

19. D – Erie

20. A – True

DID YOU KNOW?

1. Cleveland is the home of the first indoor shopping mall, the first U.S. automobile sale, and the first blood transfusion.

2. Cleveland had a WNBA team, the Cleveland Rockers, from 1997 to 2003. They were one of the original eight WNBA franchises and were owned by the same man who owned the Cavs, Gordon Gund.

3. The world's first electric traffic signal was installed at the corner of Euclid Ave. and 105th St. It was manually operated from a control booth.

4. Cleveland is not Ohio's biggest city, Columbus is. Cleveland is home to only about 383,000 people.

5. Cleveland is home to the largest Slovenian population in the United States.

6. The house from *A Christmas Story*, located in Cleveland, is now a museum. On a tour, you can see Ralphie's BB gun and Randy's snowsuit and you can even buy your own leg lamp.

7. Cleveland Public Library was the first library in the United States to allow people to check out books and take them home.

8. The Cuyahoga River is nicknamed "The River That Caught Fire" because it caught on fire 13 times.

9. President James Garfield is buried at Lake View Cemetery in Cleveland.

10. Cleveland was founded in 1796 by General Moses Cleaveland, who was the head surveyor of the Connecticut Land Company. It was named after him, but the "a" was dropped.

CHAPTER 17:

BULLET BOB

QUIZ TIME!

1. Where was Bob Feller born?

    a. Muncie, Indiana

    b. Boise, Idaho

    c. Van Meter, Iowa

    d. Brookings, South Dakota

2. Bob Feller spent his entire 18-year MLB career with the Cleveland Indians.

    a. True

    b. False

3. What year was Bob Feller elected to the National Baseball Hall of Fame?

    a. 1961

    b. 1962

    c. 1963

    d. 1965

4. How many times did Bob Feller lead the MLB in strikeouts?

    a. 3
    b. 5
    c. 6
    d. 7

5. How many times did Bob Feller lead the American League in wins?

    a. 3
    b. 5
    c. 6
    d. 7

6. What year did Bob Feller lead the American League in ERA?

    a. 1938
    b. 1939
    c. 1940
    d. 1941

7. Bob Feller missed the 1942, 1943, and 1944 MLB seasons due to military service.

    a. True
    b. False

8. How many MLB All-Star Games was Bob Feller named to?

    a. 2
    b. 4
    c. 6
    d. 8

9. How many no-hitters did Bob Feller throw?

    a. 0
    b. 1
    c. 3
    d. 5

10. Bob Feller's No. ___ is retired by the Cleveland Indians.

    a. 9
    b. 14
    c. 19
    d. 21

11. How many strikeouts did Bob Feller collect in his MLB career?

    a. 2,481
    b. 2,581
    c. 2,681
    d. 2,781

12. Bob Feller was a 1948 World Series champion.

    a. True
    b. False

13. What year did Bob Feller win a pitching Triple Crown?

    a. 1940
    b. 1941
    c. 1945
    d. 1955

14. Bob Feller was on the cover of the April 1937 issue of
_____ magazine.

    a. Popular Photography
    b. Life
    c. Sports Illustrated
    d. Time

15. How old was Bob Feller when he made his MLB debut?

    a. 17
    b. 18
    c. 20
    d. 21

16. In 2010, the "Cleveland Indians Man of the Year Award"
    was renamed the "Bob Feller Man of the Year Award."

    a. True
    b. False

17. How many complete games did Bob Feller throw?

    a. 259
    b. 269
    c. 279
    d. 289

18. How many shutouts did Bob Feller throw?

    a. 33
    b. 44
    c. 55
    d. 66

19. Bob Feller became the first pitcher to win 24 games in a season before the age of ____.

    a. 18

    b. 19

    c. 21

    d. 24

20. Bob Feller bypassed the minor leagues entirely.

    a. True

    b. False

QUIZ ANSWERS

1. C – Van Meter, Iowa

2. A - True

3. B – 1962

4. D – 7

5. C – 6

6. C – 1940

7. A – True

8. D – 8

9. C – 3

10. C – 19

11. B – 2,581

12. A – True

13. A – 1940

14. D – *Time*

15. A – 17

16. True

17. C – 279

18. B – 44

19. C – 21

20. A – True

DID YOU KNOW?

1. "The Indians of the 40s and 50s were the face of the city of Cleveland and Bob was the face of the Indians. But Bob transcended more than that era. In this day of free agency and switching teams, Bob Feller remained loyal to the city and the team for over 70 years. You will likely not see that kind of mutual loyalty and admiration ever again." – Jim Hegan

2. Bob Feller died in 2010. The Indians wore a patch based on his pitching motion the following season.

3. There is a Bob Feller Museum in his hometown of Van Meter, Iowa. It was designed by Feller's son, Stephen.

4. When serving in the Navy, Feller pitched for the Norfolk Naval Station's Bluejackets baseball team.

5. When discharged as a chief petty officer in 1945, Feller had six campaign ribbons and eight battle stars. He was an honorary member of the Green Berets later in his life.

6. Feller pitched a no-hitter on Opening Day of the 1940 season against the Chicago White Sox.

7. In high school, Feller was the starting center for the basketball team.

8. Bob Feller was elected the inaugural president of the MLB Players' Association.

9. Stan Musial called Feller "probably the greatest pitcher of our era."

10. Ted Williams called Feller "the fastest and best pitcher I ever saw during my career."

CHAPTER 18:

LITTLE O

QUIZ TIME!

1. Where was Omar Vizquel born?

    a. Oaxaca, Mexico

    b. San Juan, Puerto Rico

    c. Santo Domingo, Dominican Republic

    d. Caracas, Venezuela

2. Omar Vizquel is a member of the National Baseball Hall of Fame.

    a. True

    b. False

3. How many seasons did Omar Vizquel play in the majors?

    a. 20

    b. 22

    c. 24

    d. 26

4. What year was Omar Vizquel born?

   a. 1967
   b. 1968
   c. 1969
   d. 1970

5. How many MLB All-Star Games was Omar Vizquel named to?

   a. 3
   b. 6
   c. 8
   d. 10

6. How many Gold Glove Awards did Omar Vizquel win?

   a. 10
   b. 11
   c. 12
   d. 15

7. Omar Vizquel never won a World Series championship.

   a. True
   b. False

8. Omar Vizquel made his MLB debut against the _____.

   a. Los Angeles Dodgers
   b. Kansas City Royals
   c. Oakland Athletics
   d. Texas Rangers

9. Omar Vizquel is ____ all-time in games played at the shortstop position.

    a. 1st

    b. 2nd

    c. 3rd

    d. 4th

10. Omar Vizquel was the captain of the _____ Venezuelan World Baseball Classic team.

    a. 2004

    b. 2005

    c. 2006

    d. 2007

11. What year was Omar Vizquel inducted into the Cleveland Indians Hall of Fame?

    a. 2012

    b. 2014

    c. 2016

    d. 2018

12. Omar Vizquel is second in hits by a shortstop, behind Derek Jeter.

    a. True

    b. False

13. How many bases did Omar Vizquel steal?

    a. 353

    b. 384

    c. 404

    d. 414

14. What is Omar Vizquel's career batting average?

    a. .272
    b. .282
    c. .292
    d. .302

15. How many hits did Omar Vizquel collect?

    a. 2,777
    b. 2,877
    c. 2,977
    d. 3,077

16. Omar Vizquel played for the Cleveland Indians for 11 seasons, the most of any team he played for.

    a. True
    b. False

17. During his 24-year MLB career, Omar Vizquel played for the Cleveland Indians, Seattle Mariners, San Francisco Giants, Chicago White Sox, Texas Rangers and the

    _____.

    a. Florida Marlins
    b. San Diego Padres
    c. Los Angeles Dodgers
    d. Toronto Blue Jays

18. Omar Vizquel won ___ American League championships with the Cleveland Indians.

    a. 0
    b. 1

c. 2

d. 3

19. Omar Vizquel won ___ American League Central Division championships with the Cleveland Indians.

    a. 3

    b. 6

    c. 7

    d. 8

20. On November 18, 2013, the Detroit Tigers hired Omar Vizquel to be their first base coach.

    a. True

    b. False

QUIZ ANSWERS

1. D – Caracas, Venezuela

2. B – False

3. C – 24

4. A – 1967

5. A – 3

6. B – 11

7. A – True

8. C – Oakland Athletics

9. A – 1st

10. C – 2006

11. B – 2014

12. A – True

13. C – 404

14. A – .272

15. B – 2,877

16. A – True

17. D – Toronto Blue Jays

18. C – 2

19. B – 6

20. A – True

DID YOU KNOW?

1. Omar Vizquel was the oldest shortstop to receive a Gold Glove Award both in 2005 (age 38) and in 2006 (age 39).

2. Omar Vizquel is the all-time hits leader among players from Venezuela.

3. Omar Vizquel was chosen as one of the four greatest Indians in franchise history for the 2015 MLB All-Star Game's "Franchise Four."

4. Omar Vizquel holds the record for most double plays made while playing shortstop.

5. A feud erupted between Omar Vizquel and José Mesa after the release of Vizquel's autobiography. In the book, Vizquel criticized Mesa's performance in Game 7 of the 1997 World Series.

6. Omar Vizquel is a member of the Hispanic Heritage Baseball Museum Hall of Fame.

7. In 1996, Omar Vizquel won a Hutch Award, which is given to the MLB player who "best exemplifies the fighting spirit and competitive desire" of Fred Hutchinson by persevering through adversity." He was the first and only non-American player to win the award.

8. Omar Vizquel won the 2006 Willie Mac (Willie McCovey) Award, which is given annually to a San Francisco Giants player based on his spirit and leadership.

9. Omar Vizquel is tied for the American League record of most hits in a nine-inning game. He had 6 on August 31, 2004.

10. Omar Vizquel has the third most career assists at shortstop.

CONCLUSION

Learn anything new? Now you truly are the ultimate Indians fan! Not only did you learn about the Tribe of the modern era but you also expanded your knowledge back to the early days of the franchise.

You learned about the Indians' origins and their history, along with their journey to the present day. You learned about the history of their uniforms and jersey numbers, you identified some famous quotes, and read some of the craziest nicknames of all time. You learned more about powerhouse hitter Jim Thome, shortstop Omar Vizquel, and legendary pitcher Bob Feller.

You were amazed by Indians stats and recalled some of the most famous Indians trades and drafts/draft picks of all time. You broke down your knowledge by outfielders, infielders, pitchers, and catchers. You looked back on the Indians' championships, playoff feats, and the awards that came before, after, and during them. You also learned about the Indians' fiercest rivalries both within their division and outside it.

Every team in MLB has a storied history but the Indians have one of the most memorable of all. They have won two World

Series championships with the backing of their devoted fans.

Being the ultimate Indians fan takes knowledge and a whole lot of patience, which you tested with this book. Whether you knew every answer or were stumped by several questions, you learned some of the most interesting history that the game of baseball has to offer.

The deep history of the Indians represents what we all love about the game of baseball. The heart, the determination, the tough times, and the unexpected moments, plus the players who inspire us and encourage us to do our best because, even if you get knocked down, there is always another game and another day.

With players like Francisco Lindor, José Ramirez, and Carlos Santana, the future for the Indians continues to look bright. They have a lot to prove but there is no doubt that this franchise will continue to be one of the most competitive teams in Major League Baseball year after year.

It's a new decade, which means there is a clean slate, ready to continue writing the history of the Cleveland Indians. The ultimate Indians fans cannot wait to see what's to come for their beloved Tribe.